Presented to me by me to mark 20 years of retirement from April 1991 to April 2011.

D A Earl

MATEVŽ LENARČIČ

JANEZ BIZJAK

THE ALPS

A Bird's-Eye View

PANALP

Apart from the
Mediterranean,
the Alps are Europe's
biggest ecosystem.

The Alps are a strategic European treasury of drinking water.

Over the past
150 years,
we have lost
about half of the
Alpine ice cover.

The important
requirement
for the future
of the Alps
is development
in harmony
with nature,
emphasizing the
principle that
"less is more".

WWW.PANALP.NET

MATEVŽ LENARČIČ

JANEZ BIZJAK

THE
ALPS
A Bird's-Eye View

FOREWORD

Koïchiro Matsuura

Director-General of UNESCO

The spectacular biological and cultural diversity of the Alps – Europe's most renowned mountain range - is truly astounding. It encompasses glaciers and vineyards, financial hubs and farming communities, and prehistoric sites and contemporary art museums. Eight major languages and numerous dialects are spoken by the region's thirteen million inhabitants. Yet this unique geo-cultural entity has retained its overall unity thanks to centuries of social, religious and cultural intermingling, as reflected in its distinctive traditions, architecture and other cultural expressions, which frequently ignore the borders of the eight Alpine countries. The informative texts and stunning aerial photographs of *The Alps – A Bird's-Eye View* do much to foster greater awareness about this fascinating region and its sustainable development.

As I emphasized during the World Mountain Forum (Paris and Chambery 2000) and the United Nations International Year of Mountains (2002), UNESCO attaches great importance to the preservation of the world's mountain regions. Indeed, the promotion of innovative approaches towards the sustainable development of such areas and the protection of their human and natural resources remain high on our agenda.

In this regard, activities undertaken in conjunction with the six Alpine countries (Austria, France, Germany, Italy, Slovenia and Switzerland) that have ratified the 1972 World Heritage Convention have paved the way for the inscription of a dozen cultural and natural sites on UNESCO's prestigious World Heritage List. They include the fossil site of Monte San Giorgio and the glacial formations of the Jungfrau-Aletsch-Bietschhorn mountain area in Switzerland, the Hallstatt-Dachstein Salzkammergut Cultural Landscape in Austria, and the Rhaetian Railway in the Albula/Bernina Landscapes, a transboundary property between Italy and Switzerland. In 2000 and 2001, the Convention's signatory countries from the Alpine region convened in Hallstatt (Austria) and Turin (Italy) respectively to discuss a common framework for future transnational serial nominations of the region's most outstanding sites. Recent discussions have focused on integrating two national parks – La Vanoise in France and Gran Paradiso in Italy – into a broader serial World Heritage Alps nomination. Regarding the Alpine Convention of 1991, UNESCO regularly advises the Convention's working group on issues related to World Heritage.

UNESCO welcomes the fact that the project *The Alps – A Bird's-Eye View* also strives to promote sustainable and responsible tourism. This resonates strongly with the United Nations Millennium Development Goal 7 to ensure environmental sustainability. UNESCO contributes to this objective through the activities of the World Heritage Centre and the Man and Biosphere (MAB) programme, which adopts an interdisciplinary approach to capacity-building and research on environmental issues in conjunction with its World Network of Biosphere Reserves. UNESCO therefore wholeheartedly supports the project *The Alps – A Bird's-Eye View.*

I would like to congratulate Austria, France, Germany, Italy, Liechtenstein, Monaco, Slovenia and Switzerland, and the regional parks and organizations such as the Panalp Institute for their valuable contributions, which will also be presented in multimedia form and as a travelling exhibition. I trust that this excellent initiative will generate greater recognition of the exceptional nature of the Alpine region and help to safeguard this fascinating geo-cultural space in all of its diversity for future generations. Furthermore, I hope that this lavishly illustrated publication will inspire readers to make the journey to the Alps to behold their majesty first-hand. I am confident that those who venture to this remarkable part of our planet will discover not only a destination of incomparable beauty but also an outstanding testimony to our shared heritage.

FOREWORD

Sir Christian Bonington

The Alps are a unique mountain range because of their size and geographical position. They are at the right latitude and height to have permanent snow and extensive glaciers. They also have a geological mix to give an amazing range of different rock formations – of jagged granite spires, limestone walls and towers and many other rock formations in between - all of this within easy reach of population centres around Western Europe, with deep valleys leading into their heart to give ease of access. It adds up to a compact mountain range of quite extraordinary beauty and variety, which arches its way from the Ligurian Sea to the Adriatic in a magnificent protective arch above the Italian peninsula.

It also has a rich history and culture. In the days of Roman civilization, it provided a natural defence for Italy, though one which could be breached by the bold and brave, as was seen in the case of Hannibal during the Punic Wars, in the final collapse of the Roman Empire and much more recently, of Napoleon in the Italian campaign that confirmed his genius. In the twentieth century Switzerland was able to benefit from its mountain fastness to remain neutral in both world wars.

In early times, the high mountains themselves were perceived as the unattainable abodes of gods or devils. Hunters for chamois and crystal collectors ventured on their glaciers and the lower slopes but the high summits remained inviolate. And yet there is something in the make-up of man that draws him to the heights and makes him respond to challenge – the reason in part for the success of homo sapiens on the face of the planet. This spirit found expression in 1786, when Paccard, a scientist, and Balmat, a crystal collector, found their way to the summit of Mont Blanc. It was an incredible achievement, a huge step into the unknown; in many ways, even greater than that of Hillary and Tenzing on Everest in 1953. Interestingly, the height difference from Chamonix, where they started their ascent, to the summit of Mont Blanc is similar to the height gain from the Everest Base Camp to the summit, though admittedly climbers start at a much greater height above sea level.

It was not long before ascents of Mont Blanc became commonplace, but it was not regarded as a sport and the early pioneers felt they were fulfilling their adventurous instincts in the name of science, carrying bulky thermometers, barometers and plain tables to the tops of all their mountains. At the same time the Alps were becoming an increasingly popular destination for tourists. This was encouraged by the Romantic movement and a visit to the Alpine valleys became very much part of the grand tour.

Climbing as a sport without any scientific excuse was very much the invention of the English. In the mid nineteenth century, British gentlemen and a few ladies of some leisure began travelling to the Alps to climb peaks for enjoyment. From the beginning their endeavours were based on engaging local guides, who knew the approaches to the mountains and were tough and nimble, though they had little more experience of the high snow peaks than did their clients. As a result the relationship between experienced client and guide was very much that of partnership.

The story of the development of the Alps as a climbers' paradise would fill several volumes but to pick out a few major developments in this evolution, that of guideless climbing was of great significance. In this respect the English climber A.F. Mummery was one of the leading exponents. A brilliant natural climber, he initially used guides to make some of his great first ascents in the Alps and the Caucasus in the late nineteenth century, but realized that the core satisfaction from climbing depended on taking total responsibility for all one's decisions and being out in front, taking the lead.

Another major breakthrough started in the Eastern Alps, where the steepness of the limestone walls of the Austrian Alps, the Dolomites and the Julian Alps demanded more advanced techniques. The use of pitons for aid and protection was introduced and climbing standards rocketed. This was something the traditionalists of Western Europe in general and of Britain in particular resisted as unethical, and as a result they were left behind, particularly in the period between the First and Second World War, when climbers from Germany and Austria began climbing the great north faces of the Alps – the Schmid brothers on the Matterhorn, Meier and Peters on the Grandes Jorasses, Heckmair, Vörg, Kasperek and Harrer on the Eiger, which proved the toughest and most dangerous of all, needing four attempts at the cost of eight lives before it was finally climbed.

Climbing, as with all sport, has always been used by politicians to press their own causes. This was particularly the case between the wars and as a result the achievements of the pioneers of the time have been prejudiced by accusations of nationalistic overtones, though I'm convinced that most, if not all the climbers themselves were doing it for the sheer love of climbing and pushing the limits, with some good healthy ego thrown in.

I came on the scene in the immediate post-war period, when all the great North Walls had been climbed but there was still huge potential for new routes throughout the breadth of the Alps. I started climbing in 1951, when still at a London day school. I hitch-hiked up to the mountains of Wales and Scotland, stayed in youth hostels and climbed with anyone I could find, some experienced and some who knew no more than I did. It was a wonderful apprenticeship, learning the fundamentals of rock and ice climbing. There was no question of going abroad for my family didn't have enough money for foreign travel, but I joined the army and in 1956 was stationed in Munster, Westphalia. My first trip to the Alps was in the early summer, when I caught a train to Berchtesgaden and started to look for someone to climb with. Back in the fifties it was just a sleepy village. Such is the freemasonry of climbing that I soon stumbled across fellow climbers and even joined a group planning to climb the East Face of the Watzmann. The weather defeated us but I had my first taste of Alpine climbing.

Later on that season I went to the Dolomites with an army friend and we tasted classics like the East Face Direct of Catinaccio, the Dibona Kante on the Cima Grande and the Spigola Giallo on the Cima Picola. It was a wonderful taste of what the Dolomites have to offer, with something of history thrown in with the galleries and tunnels built during the First World War. At this time my bible was Herman Buhl's *Nanga Parbat Pilgrimage*. He told of his adventures and first ascents around the Eastern Alps on routes that I could now aspire to.

Three years later I returned to climb the Brandler Hasse route on the North Face of the Cima Grande. It had only been climbed the year before and had the reputation of being one of the hardest routes in the Dolomites, with most of the pitches being climbed using aid. We had two bivouacs and were stretched to the limit. Alex Huber from Berchtesgaden recently climbed it free and solo in a matter of hours – a sign of the way climbing has developed in the last forty-five years.

In 1957, I had my first visit to the North Wall of the Eiger. It was undoubtedly premature for my Alpine experience was negligible, but at least my climbing partner, Hamish MacInnes, was one of the best British alpinists of that time. To my great relief, we were turned back by a change in the weather before we had barely started, and we went on to climb in the Mont Blanc massif. This was just before the rescue of Longhi and Corti, who had been caught high on the Face by bad weather.

In the following years I built up my experience of alpinism, climbing with some great British climbers and in the footsteps of many of the greatest Continental alpinists. I climbed the South West Pillar of the Drus with Hamish MacInnes, Don Whillans and Paul Ross from Britain and Walter Philip and Richard Blach from Austria. The first ascent had been made only three years before by the brilliant Italian climber Walter Bonatti, who climbed it solo. It had only had three other ascents and we were the first Britons. We took three days and we couldn't help marvelling at Bonatti's boldness, skill and fortitude.

Other climbs followed around the Mont Blanc massif, confirming in my mind that the massif was the "jewel in the crown" of the entire Alpine range in terms of scenic beauty, quality and variety of climbing, and in the sheer richness of its climbing history. In 1961, Whillans, the Yorkshire climber, Ian Clough, the Pole Jan Djuglosz and myself made the first ascent of the Central Pillar on the south side of Mont Blanc at the head of the Freney Glacier. It is the highest and most remote rock feature in the Alps and in climbing it, we were drawing on the past experience of some of the best climbers of France and Italy who had been there before us – Bonatti, Desmaison, Julienne, Mazeaud, Piussi and others. They found the way to its foot and up its approach buttress to where it slimmed down to a slender candle of almost featureless granite but had been turned back. On one attempt the team of which Bonatti was a member had been caught by a ferocious storm. Four had died in the retreat. We profited from their experience, were fortunate with the weather and thanks to a brilliant bit of climbing by Don Whillans were able to climb to the top of the Pillar and over Mont Blanc. It was one of the most satisfying climbs I have ever made.

And there were others. I climbed the Walker Spur the following year. The first ascent had been made in 1938 by Riccardo Cassin, L. Espositi and U. Tizzoni. Although not reaching the highest point of the Jorasses and not as long and complex as the Croz Spur, it is by far the most attractive line – indeed it is one of the best routes in the Alps up superb granite all the way. Cassin is undoubtedly one of the greatest climbers of all time with an impressive list of first ascents across the Alps to his credit. I could almost feel his presence as we made our climb. We had a quick ascent – about seven hours – and just didn't want it to end, and so we bivouacked on the summit and the next day traversed the Grandes Jorasses and the Rochefort Ridge to the Torino Hut. There is something very special about long ridge traverses – you are moving together most of the time and there is a sense of fluid movement as you scramble over rocky gendarmes, past precipitous drops with an ever-changing view of the peaks around – the jagged teeth of the Aiguilles de Chamonix, the stately snow-clad mass of Mont Blanc, the sinuous glaciers far below.

Three days later we were at the foot of the North Wall of the Eiger and this time everything worked out. It was my fifth attempt. The weather was perfect, the face in good condition and we were on the top of our form. The climb was a delight. By modern standards it is not technically hard climbing but it combines so many different challenges. The route finding is complex, as it winds its way up the weaknesses on this huge wall. You have to be in the right place at the right time to avoid stone fall and if the weather does change, the face can change into a huge waterfall if it's warm or an avalanche of snow if it's cold. Today, after many ascents, it is still a serious climb and one of the great test pieces of the Alps.

These are some of my own personal experiences climbing in the Alps over a period of fifty years. Today, inevitably, there are changes. All the great lines have been climbed, though people still find new routes. With helicopter rescue the climbing is less serious than it was in the fifties – there is a much greater chance of being picked off the climb if things go wrong. Climate change has had its effect too. The glaciers are receding, the ice fields shrinking, stone fall is a more serious issue. The great mixed routes can only be tackled in reasonable safety in the spring and autumn. There are more bolt-protected routes on the big rock walls, something that I do question. To me one of the joys of climbing is to venture onto a face or ridge accepting what is there, using the existing cracks, ideally for hand-placed pieces of protection to safeguard progress. In doing this, we are accepting what the rock or ice environment has to offer. We are not imposing ourselves upon it but working with the environment and accordingly

accepting and judging the risks involved. Once we start placing bolts wherever we choose, not only are we controlling or even removing any risk, we are also imposing ourselves and our will upon the mountain environment. I know this is a complex and controversial subject and there are many different views, but I do believe it is something that all of us who love the mountains and mountaineering should discuss.

But whatever arguments we have over climbing ethics, however much the climate might change, the mountains of the Alps maintain their wondrous beauty, as this magnificent *Bird's-Eye View* captures. We must all strive to defend and protect not only the scenery as seen from a distance, but also the close detail, the fauna and flora, the Alpine meadows and wild forests, the character of towns and villages in their valleys and upon their flanks. In many ways one could describe the Alps as the heart and lungs of Western Europe – a place for people to relax, to be inspired, renewed, to stretch themselves to their limits, should they so desire.

This is what this beautiful book has captured.

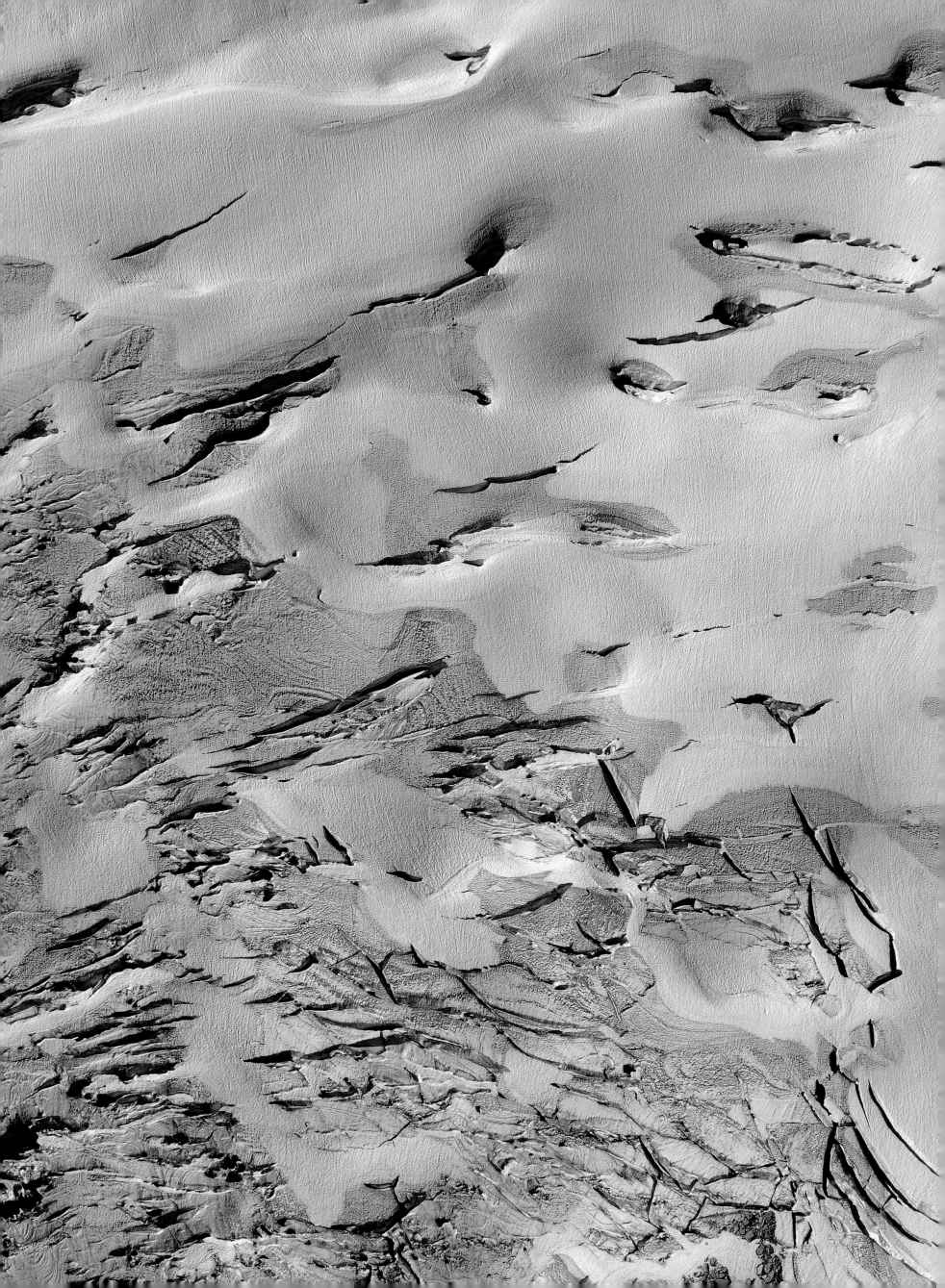

FOREWORD

Marco Onida

Secretary-General of the Alpine Convention

The Alps have always occupied a role of primary importance in the history of the European continent. Their history, so rich in events, and their unique features as a treasury of natural and cultural diversity make this one of the most interesting, as well as one of the most beautiful regions of the world.

It is no surprise that the word "Alp" is part of the world's vocabulary, whether indicating mountain climbing (alpinism) or a mountainous environment (alpine). No other mountain range has so often been the subject of poems, stories, songs, academic studies. From Petrarch to Goethe, the Alps are alive in literature. Alpine anthropology is a subject in itself in several universities.

The Alps today are a living place for some 13 million people in almost 6000 municipalities and the economic environment for crucial sectors such as tourism and mountain agriculture.

The world has globalized at an incredibly rapid pace in recent years, and today the tourist has many more alternatives than in the past, but there are still many reasons to continue exploring and living in the Alps. Their cultures, spread over several linguistic areas, represent a unique world heritage. Their history, their abundance of natural values, their uncontaminated soil, water and air, their fauna, flora and habitats, and their tranquillity all combine to make this one of the most valuable places in the world. The produce of Alpine agriculture has great quality and excellent taste. Therefore, a visit to the Alps is a must, for a variety of reasons. Just to mention another aspect, visiting the Alps in their entirety or in part implies crossing the borders of several countries. Many of the highest and best known Alpine peaks are often borders between countries or between regions – though not between cultures.

But the Alps are also changing. Transport, energy requirements and tourism infrastructures have impacted on this region to varying degrees. The Alpine population is gradually moving to cities and to the bottom of valleys. This opens up new challenges, such as the preservation of mountain agriculture and Alpine culture. And this requires cooperative and coordinated policies. In 1991 the ministers of the eight Alpine states decided to create an international treaty for the sustainable development of the Alps: the Alpine Convention. It is one of the rare international conventions focusing on a specific portion of the world's territory. Through the Alpine Convention important decisions have been taken in the past years on crucial topics such as transport, energy, forests, agriculture and tourism. Important themes for consideration still lie ahead of us, such as the preservation of the Alpine population and culture, climate change and water management. A visit to and through the Alps is also a way to see these changes from close at hand, to increase awareness and to contribute to the preservation of the Alps in the long term. This book is an ideal open door that leads the reader into the wonderful world of the Alps.

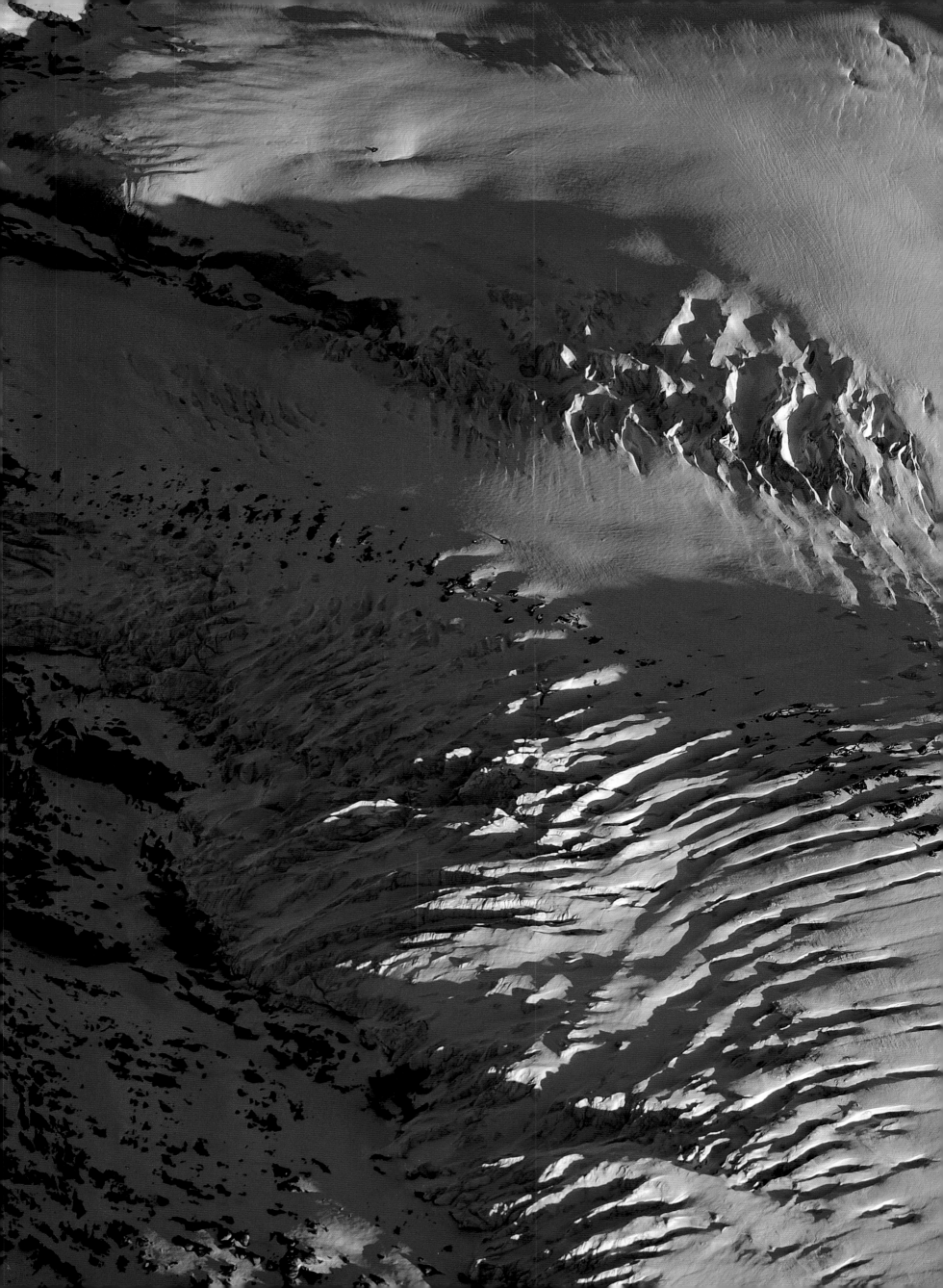

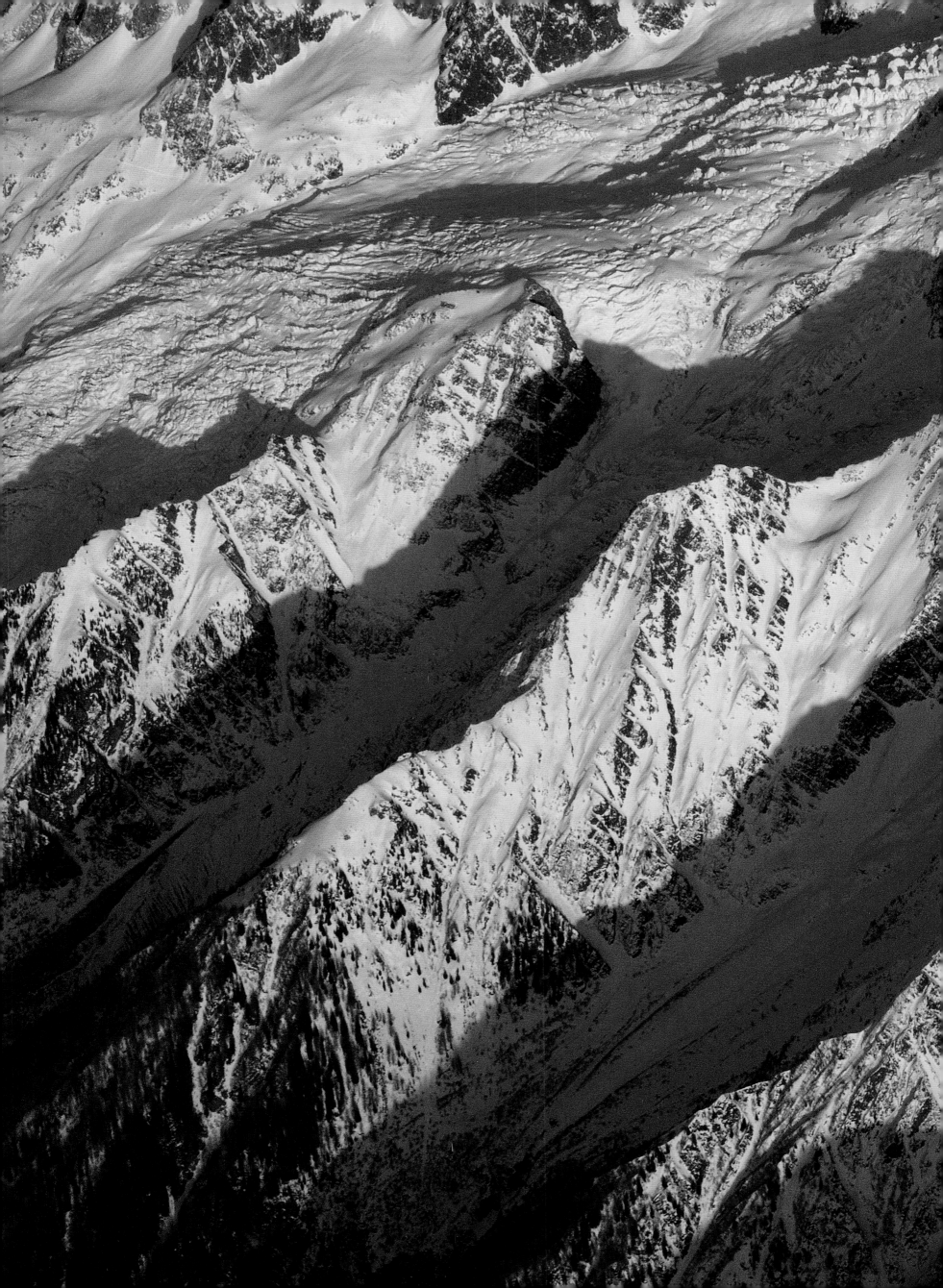

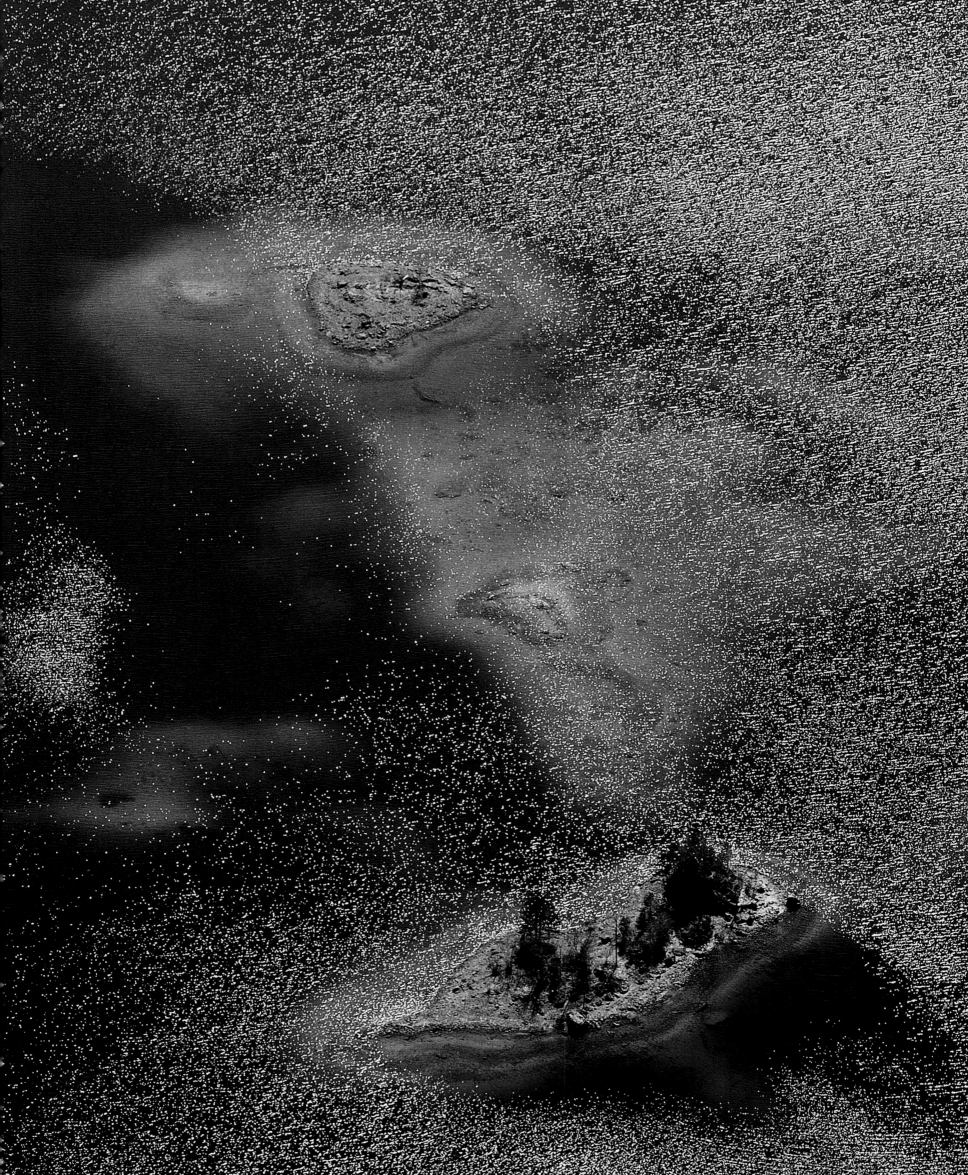

The Boka waterfall [SLOVENIA]

Janez Bizjak

THE ALPS, AS THE BIRDS SEE THEM

THE ALPS, AS THE BIRDS SEE THEM, ARE

- different Alps

- a gift from the eternal creation of the world

- a world of marvellous beauties, which have no price but unending value

- a world without borders and inaccessible to most people

- a mysterious gallery with the perfection of unique natural and cultural phenomena

- along with the Mediterranean, Europe's biggest ecosystem

- a strategic European treasury of drinking water

- with their vanishing glaciers both an indicator and relic of eternal change in nature

- a home and living space for thirteen million inhabitants speaking different languages

- a vacation and excursion destination for a hundred million visitors

- a mysterious landscape of sacred mountains and holy sites for our distant ancestors

- a mirror reflecting the special culture of survival, at least five thousand years old

- a symbol of a common cultural identity in which prehistoric, aboriginal, Germanic, Romance and Slavonic roots are intertwined.

The Alps, as the birds see them, are not

- divided into eight countries – Austria, France, Germany, Italy, Liechtenstein, Monaco, Slovenia and Switzerland

- the possession of anyone, but at the same time they are the property and good of everyone

- the monotonous kitch of tourist brochures.

BIRDS – SYMBOLS AND REALITY

Why were one-headed and two-headed eagles in the coat-of-arms of nearly all European emperors and kings the symbols of their power and inviolability? Why were supernatural properties ascribed to large birds? Even today birds are most often used in the design of the trademarks and logos of many Alpine nations and nature parks. What lies in the background of man's subconscious mythological evaluation of birds?

It was not always so. Just a century ago the slaughter of a large bird of prey was considered a courageous deed. Shocking photographs from that time show the last Bearded Vulture shot in the Alps: a few heroic men, the killers, are endeavouring to spread out the huge broken wings, and laugh in the pride of their conquest beside this exceptional trophy. For the slaughter of eagles and other large birds of prey the authorities announced special awards. Why were people afraid of them and why did they think they must be exterminated? After all, there was no documented example of an eagle attacking and tearing a person apart. The situation was similar with Alpine bears. Pictures of contented hunters, who proudly stand with one foot and a leaning gun on the head of a dead bear, are no older than thirty years. The majority were convinced that the killing was necessary, while an unsatisfied lust for trophies lurked in the background.

Nowadays these conditions are reversed. The European Union, numerous foundations and wealthy individuals finance special programmes to re-introduce big carnivors and large birds of prey, especially the Griffon Vulture and Bearded Vulture in the Alps, in their original habitat. Releases of young animals into their natural environment in the high Alps have developed into well-publicized media events. Professional symposia and conferences are organized on the content and experiences of these programmes, scientific articles are written and many books published.

Is this a sign that people are newly well-informed or an indication of a bad conscience because of unjustifiable actions in the past? Or is it altogether just an end in itself? We know

>> Continued on page 30

Ferdinand Lainer

THE BEARDED VULTURE IN THE ALPS

One of the most successful species protection projects in Europe

The decline in Bearded Vulture numbers

The Bearded Vulture once lived in practically all the mountains of southern Europe and in the Alps. Probably no other bird of prey has made such a strong impression on people, or at least this is seen in many fables and legends where the peaceful Bearded Vulture appears as a bloodthirsty creature that even attacks children. The Bearded Vulture has also been wrongly accused of killing chamois and stealing lambs, as is seen in the vernacular names "chamois robber-vulture" and "lamb vulture". Other reasons for its decline and partial extermination were the use of poisoned traps, shooting on the orders of zoological societies and in some regions the disappearance of sources of food. In the Alps the Bearded Vulture was virtually exterminated in the 19th century, surviving longest in the Western Alps, where the last proven nesting was recorded in 1910. Elsewhere in Europe the bird has survived only in the Pyrenees, and on Corsica and Crete, with some individuals also in the continental part of Greece, but there too their numbers are greatly threatened.

A 30-year-long international re-introduction project

After a lengthy and difficult search for suitable breeding material, the Alpine Zoo in Innsbruck with its former director Dr Helmut Pechlaner succeeded in rearing the first Bearded Vultures in the hatchery. This success was the foundation stone of the Bearded Vulture project and a vital contribution to one of the most important projects aimed at

protecting an animal species. On the basis of their regular breeding successes an international project for re-introducing the Bearded Vulture in the Alps was founded in 1978 with the support of the Frankfurt Zoological Society, the WWF Austria and Switzerland and the IUCN. From then until 1986 a breeding network was established which included about 30 zoos and the Richard Faust Central Station for Bearded Vulture Breeding in Haringsee (Lower Austria).

The first releases into the wild in the Hohe Tauern National Park in 1986

The international expert committee selected four widely separated locations in the Alps for releasing the Bearded Vultures. Within the framework of a study of the natural environment carried out by Swiss biologists, four Bearded Vultures were released first of all in 1986 in the Rauris/Kruml valley in the Hohe Tauern National Park. Apart from young birds in this location, two older birds were released in Argenterra (Alpi Marittime Nature Park) and two in Martello (Stilfser Joch National Park). This was followed by more releases: in Bargy/ Upper Savoy (France) in 1987, in the Swiss National Park in 1991, in the Mercantour National Park (France) and the Alpi Marittime Nature Park (Italy) in 1993, and in the Stilfser Joch National Park (Italy) in 2000. So far a total of 156 Bearded Vultures have been released in the Alps, 47 of them in the Hohe Tauern National Park. Outside the Alps three Bearded Vultures were released in Sierra de Cazorla (Andalusia), since a project of returning this raptor to the wild was started in Spain as well in 2006. In 2008 seven young Bearded Vultures were released into the wild for the first time on Sardinia.

Monitoring – supervision and public relations

An extremely important component of the project is following as accurately as possible the life of Bearded Vultures released into the wild. The method of marking used makes it possible to establish identity accurately in young birds for approximately three years up to the time they lose their immature plumage. In order to follow the life of the released birds further, permanent scientific observation was set up. Thus throughout the entire Alpine region a network of volunteer observers was put in place, drawn from local inhabitants, national park staff, hunters, ornithologists, farmers and tourists. With the aim of understanding better the journeys of young Bearded Vultures, knowledge of which had previously been rather superficial, modern satellite technology was used in the re-introduction project after 2004 for eleven young birds of prey, which were released at that time into the wild in the Swiss National Park and the Stilfser Joch National Park. A small satellite transmitter is attached to a tail feather.

In recent years genetic monitoring has also been employed within the permanent observation network. Precisely this feature has an advantage over all the other factors in the project concerning the breeding and re-introduction of Bearded Vultures. Only by means of genetic research can dangers such as the loss of genetic variability or the problem of related birds mating be brought under control. It is also important to follow the sexual relations and genetic structure of this newly settled population.

The pleasing development of the population in the Alps

Over the past years the Bearded Vulture population has developed in a very positive way. Depending on the model used for calculation, from 120 to 130 of these birds live in the Alps. The number of young birds hatched in freedom is very satisfying. The first young Bearded Vulture flew from its nest in Upper Savoy (France) in 1997, and since then the Bearded Vulture counts again as a bird breeding in the Alps. If at the beginning there was only one breeding pair, the number has now grown to 15 such pairs. In 2008 seven young birds took to flight in the Alps and the number of those hatched in freedom has grown to 50. Unfortunately this statistic also includes data on lost offspring.

The Bearded Vulture is certainly the most powerful bird of prey and with a wingspread measuring up to 2.85 metres, it is also the biggest in the Alps. Naturally, such a wingspread makes it a superb glider. The birds live in mountainous regions mostly above the tree-line. They occupy enormous hunting grounds (100-750 km^2), which they defend against others of the same species. They make their nests on rock ledges, and lay eggs in mid-winter. Generally two eggs are laid in a well-lined nest, within the space of 4 - 5 days. Approximately 54 days later, two young birds are hatched, but always only one remains alive. The bird that hatches first is stronger and acts aggressively towards its younger brother or sister, pushing it away from food. Thus the younger one becomes increasingly weaker and soon perishes (Cainism). The second egg functions only as a biological spare, therefore, in case the first bird might be sickly or perish after hatching. Both parents take turns both in hatching and rearing. The reason for the unusual time of laying eggs is the abundant possibilities for finding food while the young birds are growing. In the melting snow of spring there is plenty of game that has perished during the winter due to the cold or avalanches. After about 117 days the young Bearded Vulture first dares to fly from the nest, from mid-June to mid-July. For some weeks after that the parents still provide it with food.

Bearded Vultures are scavengers, feeding primarily on what other scavengers leave. Up to 80% of their food consists of bones, sinews and ligaments. Bones might at first seem to be less nutritious food, but actually they provide as much energy as meat. Due to the capacities of their digestive system and gastric juices, Bearded Vultures are the only raptors that can make the best use of the nutritious content of bones. Their extendable gullet enables them to swallow awkward plunder. Bones that are at first too big they grasp with their talons, carry them high up into the air and dash them on flat rocks where the bones are smashed to pieces. This is where their other name comes from – ossifrage, bone-breaker.

The Bearded Vulture – an important symbol

Bearded Vultures have become an important symbol of the Hohe Tauern National Park. On 2 August 2008 a new National Park centre was opened in Rauris entitled "Kings of the Heights", a contemporary exhibition about the life of three great birds of prey: the Bearded Vulture, Griffon Vulture and Golden Eagle.

The project for re-introducing the Bearded Vulture in the Alps is celebrating its 30th anniversary and has developed very successfully: so far 156 young birds have been released in the Alps, 52 have flown from their nests in freedom, and in 2008 15 pairs bred for the first time. This project is one of the most successful and best known connected with the re-introduction of animal species in the Alps. Bearded Vultures recognize no borders established by man. The Bearded Vulture project is thus a fine example of the international protection of nature and of animal species. It is not just a model of successful international protection of species, but also symbolizes what national parks can do in the sphere of forming awareness. Nobody in the region of a national park is afraid of these birds any more, on the contrary, everybody is delighted if they catch sight of a Bearded Vulture with majestic beats of its wings circling above the summits of our Alps.

how to get funds for high-sounding studies and promotion, we know how to ask why birds are constantly decreasing, but we pretend ignorance about the causes that drive birds away from our and their environment.

We people do not know how birds see the Alps, how they look at them and what they perceive. A bird's perspective is not a human perspective, it is only our notion of their view which we attribute to birds. "No bird flies too high, if it flies with its own wings" is an old piece of Tibetan wisdom. People are capable of flying and seeing the Alps from an altitude that birds cannot reach, but do not have the ability to land elegantly and silently like an eagle in its eyrie under a great overhang amidst sheer rock faces.

Birds do not leave any traces in the air, do not pollute the atmosphere nor change it with exhaust fumes. No-one has dared to designate birdsong as noise pollution. No-one has ever succeeded in stopping a flock of birds or altering the direction of their flight in a moment. No-one has yet discovered the logistics, organization and seasonal programming of birds' transcontinental migrations. For their flights from Scandinavia across Europe to Africa and back or from distant Asia across to the Alps they do not need satellite navigation, reliable maps or cartographic knowledge. They know where to go to and why they must go there. An instinct which no human technology can equal.

Do birds recognize the noise of traffic, which echoes high above the roads and mountain passes of the Alps? Does it disturb them, as it does most people who look for and indeed expect peace and quiet in the mountains?

Who do the Alps belong to? This question is asked only by those who do not realize that they belong to no-one in particular, yet at the same time they belong to everyone. First of all, the Alps represent the habitat of thousands of species of plants and animals, then the living space of local people, and only in the last instance a destination for relaxation and spiritual enrichment – for holiday-makers, mountaineers, sportspeople, artists and solitary travellers. The visitors are guests, who cannot divide up what is not theirs. So helicopters and aero-taxis are not owners of the air space, just as motorized tourists are not owners of the roads, and walkers in the high mountains cannot lay claim to the mountain paths. It is we people who burden and change the Alps, the birds never do.

We who live in the countryside below the Alps do not see or hear the birds who fly around us, because this is an everyday occurrence and needs no explanation. Those who live in big industrial cities also do not see or hear them, because they are no longer present.

Birds are an unmistakable and even for non-specialists an understandable indicator of natural and environmental equili-brium. Wherever there is something wrong in the atmosphere, they withdraw, depart and disappear. Like light and thought, they are a symbol of boundlessness, of inimitable virtuosity in song and flight, of tireless joy at every new morning and an example of enthusiasm for survival.

This view of the Alps as the birds see them is an attempt to make a different evaluation of these mountains; for our mental distancing and the self-questioning needed to sober up from our usual drunken blindness, assuming that everything is alright and not so bad after all. Perhaps this view from above of the marvellous beauty of the Alps will shake up even those who are indifferent at present, and stimulate them towards a different way of thinking and the realization that each of us is obliged to do something to preserve our common home.

THE CREATION OF THE ALPS – AN ON-GOING PROCESS

The Alps are material proof that there is nothing permanent in nature except constant change!

Seen from above, the relief of the Alps looks like a petrified and frozen sea, from which a vast array of archipelagoes with jagged peaks springs up, a world apparently unsuitable for life and dangerous for human beings. At one and the same time dramatic chaos and a cosmos organized with breathtaking perfection. Such are the Alps, our home and the dream of those whose home is elsewhere.

The formation of the Alps is placed by experts in a temporal framework extending over a billion years; the age of the later limestone Alps is reckoned to be a good two hundred million years, while the older mountain ranges are several times more than that. Such dimensions are unimaginable for our present-day human understanding and concept of time. We can scarcely conceive the period of the first paleolithic visitors to the Alps 40,000 years ago; the petrified fish and shells in the Dachstein limestone of the Eastern Alps that are two hundred million years old are thus quite beyond our grasp of time.

The Alps, as we see them today, are simply a photograph of a moment of time within the process of constant forming, changing and cyclical renewing and the alternation of cold periods and warmer ones. No-one knows how many cyclical changes there have been nor how many there will still be. Experts have written numerous books and weighty tomes about the formation of the Alps, about intercontinental and tectonic shifts, the pushing, rising, folding and fracturing of mountains, about the sea which covered today's summits, about the glacial grinding of the earth's surface, about the time before humans appeared, and when the world was turned upside down. It is not the purpose of this book simply to copy such data.

Avalanches, landslides and earthquakes, symbols and repeated warnings of the ceaseless changing of the Alps

The Alps are living and are still moving, the process of creation continues. We are reminded of the truth of this by earthquakes, rockfalls, landslides and the destructive rage of torrential waters. In the last fifty years a number of summits in the Eastern Alps have been broken off.

Large rockfalls change the relief, destroy forests, houses, roads. Most often they are the result and continuation of powerful earthquakes. These are typical of the Eastern Alps, especially of the Julian Alps and Carnian Alps in the restless triangle between Friuli, north-west Slovenia and Carinthia. The Villach earthquake of 1349, the Friuli earthquake of 1975 and the Posočje one of 1999 are the three best-known landmarks that draw attention to destructive and dramatic changes in the Alps. Many villages and churches have disappeared in the ruins, while jewels of folk architecture and of the irreplaceable authentic cultural heritage have been destroyed. In many places an alpine landscape has lost its identity. Even worse than the material damage are the unseen consequences: the affected inhabitants live in continual fear. No-one can avoid it, fear is transmitted from the despairing older generation to the children. Smaller shocks occurring each year after a major earthquake strengthen the uncertainty. Nobody knows when there will be a powerful earthquake again, and when the rocks above the houses will thunder down into the valley. This year, some years later, after a thousand years or even tomorrow?

Apart from earthquakes, human perseverance in the Alps has been tested and is still tested by destructive monsters which you can only observe in helplessness and be thankful if you remain alive: avalanches and landslides and the tumultuous force of deep waters. These carry away people, houses, cultivated fields, meadows, forests, roads and can wipe out a century's work in a single sweep. Every year some region of the Alps is cut off from the world for some days because of avalanches, landslides or floods. No computerized technology and no information system controlling the earth or the universe can predict, still less prevent the appalling, unbridled rage of snow, earth or water. Is this unexpected raging caused by the instability of a natural balance we cannot comprehend? As if destruction were a condition for establishing this balance.

CLIMATE

Cyclical change is a programmed process in the earth's history. We cannot prevent changes, but we can willy-nilly accelerate them ...

The current climate changes, most noticeable in the faster melting of ice in the Antarctic, are attributed to ozone holes, sunspots, the untamed increase in the release of greenhouse gases and other harmful consequences of the industrial and technological explosions. To realize and acknowledge that something is wrong also in and below the Alps, we do not need alarming pictures of huge Asian cities, where gas-masks are everyday equipment for the inhabitants; it is enough to ascend some high mountain and get a bird's-eye view of industrial cities below the Alps. In clear weather a greyish-blue layer can easily be seen covering them, a poisonous smog which is the denser, the bigger the city is. There is still time, and it all depends on people that we will not have to walk around in gas-masks below the mountains.

GLACIERS – THE DRAMATIC DISAPPEARANCE OF MYSTERIOUS GIANTS

The most noticeable relics of the endless forming and changing of the Alps are disappearing, and with them an important part of the Alpine identity is disappearing too. My generation had the good fortune to see different Alps, which are greatly changed today. When we walked along glaciers at the beginning of the 1960s, there were no signs that they would hardly exist in another fifty years' time, that in disappearing they would be reduced to an unrecognizable state. At that time nobody thought of comparing photographs of the biggest Alpine glaciers from the end of the 19th century with pictures a hundred years later. The ice and snow cover of the Alps struck us as eternal and unchanging, it aroused admiration and demanded special knowledge and equipment when you walked there. For those who lived below the mountains the glaciers were a mysterious world high above, an inaccessible and bewitched region, where humans dared not stray, could not and must not. A world of legends about gold and crystal palaces and ancient cities far beneath the ice. The tragedies of those lost under avalanches and collapsing seracs filled people with fear and caution for millenia. The word glacier used to represent the unseen movement of an apparently motionless river of ice, the cracking, rumbling and collapsing of impassable seracs, the yawning crevasses, deceptively covered with snow, and the unimaginably deep black-green abysses which swallowed the glacial waters. We called them icy giants and forgot that they were just a modest remnant of real giants, which 20,000 years ago ground out and created Alpine valleys. Now even the last memories from the ancient coming to birth of the Alps are bidding us farewell. Probably no other human generation has been given the chance to observe and follow this unexpected transformation of the Alps.

Anyone who walked fifty years ago along the Glacier Noire and Glacier Blanc in the kingdom of Les Écrins, along the Mer de Glace, Aletsch, Gorner, Morteratsch, Jochferner and

>> *Continued on page 32*

Hans Haid

THE MYTH ABOUT AVALANCHES

Sketches for a cultural history

The constant threat from the elementary forces of nature, such as avalanches, floods, debris flows and the like has been a part of life for people in the Alps for centuries and indeed millenia. Respect for the power of nature and its various forms, and attempts to find protection from that power have been an essential part of the culture and strategy of survival in many exposed places in the Alpine region from the French Maritime Alps to the Julian Alps in Slovenia.

In former times the technical solutions available gave very modest hopes of protection, and the inhabitants put more trust in their pleas, processions, vows, prayers, pilgrimages and reliance on God.

The first extensive cultural history of avalanches in the Alps tells dramatic stories of how avalanches in past centuries claimed several thousand human lives as well as exceptionally high numbers of domestic animals, destroyed many buildings and ruined the general welfare. Apart from Switzerland, no comparison has been made so far nor any documentation prepared on the past and present role of avalanches in the real battle for survival and for a local identity. In this connection we might remember events not so far back, including that in 1999 in Ischgl-Valzur and the village of Galtür in the Paznauntal valley in Tyrol with 38 dead or the 120 killed in Vorarlberg in 1954, of whom 80 perished in the small mountain village of Blons in the Großes Walsertal valley. January and February 1951 are the two months bearing the sad reputation that the greatest number of avalanches in recent history were triggered then.

There are many names which the inhabitants of the Alps know for the snow masses that roar down from the mountains into the valley. There are two main groups of avalanches: in spring there are those which can be "foreseen", and the completely unpredictable and particularly dangerous avalanches of loose snow. We know from recent calculations that the greatest speed of these dangerous avalanches can reach from 300 to 400 km per hour. This incredible speed places avalanches among the most dramatic natural phenomena; it is a deadly speed that even outstrips the worst tornadoes and hurricanes. So it is no surprise that people in the mountains, in their extremely perilous and vulnerable valleys, feel threatened and totally exposed to danger whenever snow falls for several days and nights until the snow cover is two or thee metres deep.

Especially dramatic and heart-rending, as described in authentic reports, are avalanches that created terrible havoc in certain places in the Alps. In one such narrative by a deeply affected writer in the newspaper "Grundlseer Lahn" in the Styrian Salzkammergut we read how the bodies of forest workers were dug out: "details that make one's hair stand on end … here a head appears out of the snow, there an arm, somewhere else a leg, and so on … some were horribly squashed, others lay with their heads split open." The description was both moving and dreadful, how the deeply frozen corpses could not be placed in the coffins prepared: "they were piled like hard, crooked blocks of wood, so that altogether it was terrible to look at". Most

of the bodies were just covered with blankets. The whole procession moved along for several kilometres to the cemetery in Bad Aussee. This was not referred to as a "natural catastrophe" but as a "natural event", people had made use of numerous, but mostly ineffective measures. So in their virtually complete vulnerability, they turned to non-material helps. There are testimonies of how people went time and again on pilgrimages, made pleas and vows. In the Swiss canton of Wallis "strict vows" were well-known, which forbad games and dancing, and the women could not wear coloured underwear. From Wallis and the surroundings of Chamonix there are records of how priest exorcists drove out evil spirits.

There is also evidence that really bad events led to notorious "witch trials". Hundreds, or even thousands of women and girls, and also men and boys were accused of "making the weather", found guilty and put to death.

Many stories tell of how people in the most endangered places and valleys searched for mysterious and terrible creatures. They found consolation and help in a "nymph" or "white fairy" or other mysterious female beings. All of these had the common feature of possessing good and evil linked together in equal measure. They were both avengers and protectors. In these stories women play a very important role, much greater than that of male mythological beings. These female beings certainly point to a memory of an old, in fact very old culture characterized by the matriarchate.

The ringing of bells had a very significant place in defence and protection. Simply the ringing was supposed to avert the danger. In the territory of the Alps the power of church bells is well-known everywhere, as one finds hundreds of specially dedicated, so-called "weather bells". But in the Ventertal valley in Tyrol, for instance, they took the horses' sleigh bells off in dangerous places, since the jangling could trigger avalanches at a distance.

Some of the most dramatic consequences of avalanches are also exactly described and documented. We can hardly imagine the suffering which befell the inhabitants of the places affected in such moments, since often whole villages and settlements were destroyed. To preserve the memories of these events in words and pictures for later generations, they transferred the sad scenes to votive boards, called "Marterln". Many of these are now collected and documented.

On one occasion snow buried 46 people in 11 houses in the Tyrolean valley of Lechtal; on another, 40 men and boys died under an enormous avalanche in Elmen as they brought hay down from hayhuts in the mountains. It was as if the place had been exterminated. On the Schneeberg mountain in South Tyrol, where for centuries the highest mine in Europe was situated, avalanches killed 83 miners in the years between 1500 and 1693.

In Rabenstein in the Hinterpasseiertal valley, also in South Tyrol, the inhabitants in threatened places and farmsteads celebrated special "avalanche feast-days", and during the period of greatest danger they withdrew into their own little cottages protected against avalanches. There was a similar situation in Saas Fee in the Swiss canton of Wallis. According to statistical data, avalanches took the lives of 1,592 people in the years between 1937 and 1999.

In recent decades the number of skiers and snowboarders killed has exceeded these others. Building in places and regions devoted to ski tourism was permitted to an extreme extent or even beyond it, and often even in "red" areas. These were mostly hotels and guest-houses. Then in the international press there were reports about "events of the century". Because of the dangerous terrain, mighty iron traverses had to be built in new tourist centres for protection against avalanches. The cost of these modern "protective forests" ran into many millions of euros.

Or there are events like that in 1999 in the Ötztal valley. In the interests of ski tourism avalanches were deliberately triggered by blasting, so that these huge and dangerous masses of snow thundered down into the Ventertal valley. The technology proved its worth and established new limits. We can estimate on the basis of the "cultural history" of avalanches how sensitive the high-mountain regions are and how unstable the equilibrium has become.

Anyone who has witnessed this terrifying happening will know how helpless man is in the face of a natural disaster and how avalanches are still an enigma even for the most experienced avalanche experts. When avalanches of loose snow with an unimaginable speed of 350 or 400 km per hour hurtle into the valley, carving a new route through the forests and villages, experts speak of implosion and no longer of explosion.

But why do people remain all the same in dangerous valleys? After 1999, Galtür with its new "forest" of iron traverses began an advertising campaign about "the safest Alpine village". But how safe is this Alpine village?

One chronicle concerning avalanches in the previous 300 years gives the information that several thousand people had lost their lives in this way in the Alps alone. Here is a small extract:

1602 and 1609: Davos/Switzerland - 13 and 26 dead;

1613: Galtür/Tyrol – 9 dead;

1664: Elmen /Tyrol - 42 men killed as they pulled hay;

1667: Anzonico, Tessin/Switzerland - 88 dead;

1689: apart from 1951 this counts as the worst winter in the Alps for avalanches. In Montafon in Vorarlberg 120 people died; in the whole of Austria there were 256 victims, including 15 in the Gasteinertal valley, 31 in Elbigenalp in the Tyrolean valley of Lechtal and 29 in the village of Galtür/Paznauntal. In Swiss Prätigau 57 people died;

1695: in Bosco Gurin in the canton of Tessin 34 people died;

1720: approximately 100 dead in Rueras in Graubünden / Switzerland; 40 in the region of Brig in the canton of Wallis/ Switzerland and 84 dead in Goms in the same canton;

1738: 19 forest workers were killed in Grundlsee/Styria;

1749: 64 in Rueras, the canton of Graubünden/ Switzerland and 41 in Bosco Gurin, Tessin canton;

1755: Valle Stura in Piedmont/Italy – 22 dead;

1757: Le Villard/Vallouise – 27 dead;

1788: Molines en Queyras/France – 21 dead;

1807: 18 people died in rooms in Arlberg;

1817: 19 people died in Moos and Neder in the Ötztal valley.

1885: 20 people died on the Ljubelj pass/Slovenia, about 300 in Piedmont, including approximately 80 in Frassino/Val Varaita.

In the period 1916-1918 about 40,000 died in avalanches on the mountain fronts between Slovenia and the Ortler region; some estimates put the toll as high as 80,000 soldiers.

In the bitter winter of 1950-51 30 people died in Slovenia, 98 in the Swiss Alps and 135 in Austria, 54 of them in Tyrol alone, 16 in Heiligenblut and 14 in the Gasteinertal valley (during the night of 20-21 January 1951); 19 were killed in Vals/Switzerland;

1954: 122 dead in Vorarlberg, including 80 in the Großes Walsertal valley;

1970: 74 people died in an avalanche on the Plateau d'Assy in Upper Savoy/France, of whom 56 were children in a sanatorium;

1995-96: 34 people died under avalanches in Austria, including 16 in Tyrol;

1998-99: 13 people died in the canton of Wallis/Switzerland, 38 in the villages of Galtür and Valzur in the Paznauntal valley/Tyrol, 10 in Evolène/Switzerland and 12 in Hameau de Montroc/France, etc.

Pasterze glaciers and compared their state then with the year 2008 cannot believe the shocking changes: the tongues of unrecognizably depleted glaciers have retreated far back and higher up, while the former immense ice masses have disappeared in a wilderness of moraine banks, granite rock and muddy black soil.

Is it a privilege that in forty years we experience changes that in the past lasted for centuries or millenia? Or is this a punishment and admonishment for our attitude to the environment? Self-regulating and cyclic climate changes that we cannot prevent are built into the earth's history but evidence keeps increasing to show that we have speeded up these processes through egocentric exhaustion of our planet and irresponsibly changing its surface. In the Alps as well. We only need think of the obsession with land reclamation and the levelling out of hummocky meadows or the bulldozer disfigurement of the high mountains for the needs of new ski centres.

Half of Europe is supplied with drinking water from the ice and snow cover of the Alps.

The water that flows from the bellies of glaciers is as old as the ice on the first bottom layers, that is, 12,000 years from the last glacial period. We are drinking the history of the Alps. For how much longer?

Instead of taking serious measures, we lose time and energy with measurements and accumulating data and statistical graphs on the shrinking of the glaciers. We do not dare to restrict or stop skiing on glaciers and admit that this is simply an abuse of the ice miracle for commercial purposes and for the snobbish extension of skiing enjoyment far into the summer. We have seen attempts at saving the glaciers by shielding them with gigantic protective covers. As if covering them with a shroud. But this was not rescuing the glaciers but the ski slopes on them.

We can imagine what the Alps were like 20,000 years ago and to what altitude the valleys were covered with ice whenever spring or autumn fogs cover the valley region, from which only the highest peaks jut out. The upper edge of that sea of fog is like the surface of ancient glaciers that return to the present and play with images of the future. The last glacial period was not the only one nor will it be the final one.

When the glaciers disappear, the dark brown backcloth of sharp granite peaks will remain. The snow-white trademark of the Alps will darken into black. Literally! Due to the colour of silicate rocks. Only the mountains in the Eastern Alps will remain white, those of limestone and dolomite. Will the Alps then be distinguished by colour? The Black Alps instead of the Western and Central Alps and the White Alps instead of the Eastern Alps?

WATER IN THE ALPS – THE ARTERIES OF OUR SURVIVAL

Water: the single relevant question of survival for all cultures and all civilizations in every age up to our day. Water has remained the greatest wealth of the Alps. We forget how precious it is in the rocky regions of the Mediterranean and how people in the deserts and parched areas of the world have to walk for days or even weeks to find water. We do not realize that the amount of water we pour away every day in Europe represents an entire fortune for several hundreds of millions who live on the other side of the world; for many it is an inaccessible condition for survival.

The barely visible capillaries and twisting streams in high valleys, which are linked with big rivers to supply the Mediterranean, the Black Sea and the North Sea, appear from great heights like the veins and arteries of an unearthly organism. Along with fire, water is nature's greatest mystery. The condition for the birth and existence of all that lives.

There is no oil in the Alps, but they are endowed with an abundance of pure water, such as wealthy oil sheiks in Arabian deserts dream of in vain. Today it is oil that mercilessly dictates world politics, but we forget that water was and still is the basis of human survival. Who knew 200 years ago what oil is? And 200 years later it will probably only be mentioned in history books. People will live without it, just as they did before they heard about it. When there is no oil capital left, there will not be any money for expensive facilities to obtain drinking water from sea water. The history of humankind was created by great civilizations so long as they had water. They disappeared when dramatic natural changes caused water to disappear.

The lowland regions of Europe already experience a lack of water due to summer droughts or water becomes contaminated because of senseless intensive farming. The level of the water-table falls ever lower. When the situation is at its worst, people in endangered areas are supplied with bottles of drinking water, which are filled in the Alps, or water tanks are driven to them from distant subalpine places. Where will we go for water if the supply in the Alps runs dry?

We have created a myth about the Alps as a strategic European treasury of drinking water. But the myth is disappearing, the treasury is emptying, because it is not locked up in a carefully protected gallery, but is becoming a sales article. The awareness of water as the greatest capital of the third millenium is changing into a threadbare phrase at many professional workshops and simposia. Influential decision-makers, who have the power, financial capacity and opportunity to do something concrete to preserve and protect our common bounty, our shared treasure, do nothing. Self-satisfied public appearances with fine-sounding but empty words that commit us to nothing provide the surest way of changing nothing in our heads. And for this reason everything can change in nature.

We have varied attitudes to Alpine waters. Some, obsessed with avarice and marketing plans, would lay pipes at every virgin jet of water, every waterfall, every foaming gorge and every kind of wild water dance, to capture the unrepeatable miracle of water, which is the property of everybody, and enterprisingly sell it to us, changed into kilowatt hours. And at the same time they would let filtered faeces and other waste material flow through our water pipes. Others do not know how to see and understand this profitability and besides electrical energy we need the kind of energy that only primeval water can give, whether standing, falling or flowing, quiet or with a deafening roar, rushing or lazy, among rocks or in the grass, crystal clear or muddied by storms, foaming or charmed into a motionless mirror.

We do not appreciate what has been given to us. I was personally struck on seeing a tourist from a city of several million inhabitants, who stopped by the crystal-clear, turquoise waters of the river Soča in the Julian Alps. Kneeling on the gravel, he excitedly scooped up the water in his cupped hands and ceremoniously raised it to his lips. Accustomed to a river that flowed sluggishly through his city, hidden beneath a thick foamy, slimy layer of stinking effluent, and to a city water supply that provides only water for cooking and washing, he had never seen and could not believe that there was still rushing water anywhere in the world, which you simply take and drink without fear. And quench your thirst without needing to buy a plastic bottle.

THE CULTIVATION AND SETTLEMENT OF THE ALPS

The first visitors, the forming of the cultural landscape

We do not know what the first highlanders, the first visitors to this mountain world, were like. Discovering and gaining knowledge of the mountains was not a recreational activity for those who dared to venture into the unknown wilderness, but was driven by the merciless need for survival. Whoever hesitated, disappeared and was missed by few. Hunters, shepherds, the strange, solitary yet knowledgeable searchers for mineral ores, collectors of ores, and miners, who died in the labyrinths of mountain mines, searchers for medicinal herbs, packmen and merchants between the Mediterranean and the Baltic, smugglers and traders, pilgrims and penitents, in the modern age scientists and finally tourists. Such was the order in which they came.

The first inhabitants of the Alps to be discovered and documented so far were cave hunters in the late paleolithic age, i.e. 30,000 to 50,000 years ago. Professionally they are termed Homo sapiens sapiens or Cro-Magnons, after the French archeological site Cro-Magnon. At that time the Alpine valleys were under a several-hundred-metre-thick cover of ice, so that the caves which they made their dwelling places were accessible almost directly from the ice surface. Nowadays the glaciers no longer exist, so these caves seem from the valleys to be high up in the mountains. In the cave sediments, several metres deep, evidence of the first visitors was found: remains of hearths, simple stone and bone tools (needles and arrows), and the bones of extinct animals, predominantly the cave bear *(Ursus spelaeus)*.

Hervé Cortot

ENCLOSURES IN THE CHAMPSAUR

Les Écrins (France), a symbol of the high mountains, a fortress in this rugged world on the margin of the Southern Alps, a massif in a spacious, uninhabited region. And not only that! The photo does indeed show us the lofty summits that rise up to 4000 m and the mighty glaciers, but an observant traveller will notice some special characteristics of the landscape close to hand.

The view from the Bayard pass (1248 m) or Manse pass (1263 m) first leads the eye onwards to the peaks of Le Sirac and Vieux Chaillol, but somewhere below them it chances on a surprising picture in which hedges, clustered villages, rectangles of cultivated earth and meadows are interwoven; this is a landscape that testifies to diligent farmers. The wilderness is tamed: each mountain stream, as well as the Drac, is hemmed in by riparian vegetation, and this is linked with the irregular pattern formed by the rectangles of land intended for polyculture and stock-breeding. Everything is connected with care for water: channels, ponds for watering the cattle, mills and their "rounds". All the details have the same purpose: usefulness, creating conditions for self-sufficient farming, for a long time the only activity of the considerable population, which settled here at an altitude between 1000 and 1500 m.

Nowadays the polyculture has given way to the breeding of cattle and sheep. Champsaur is famous for milk and meat. Signs of progressive modernization are evident: big buildings which have nothing in common with the traditional ones scattered at random in the cluster village. Some pig breeding can be added. Nevertheless, most of the fodder for the animals is so far home-produced.

Clearly the contemporary economy is no longer linked with the type of countryside. As agricultural and environmental measures were introduced, the farmers talked about certain features of their daily lives: the water source, the hedge as protection for the livestock from wind and sun. But nothing about the things that underlie the typical arrangement of the countryside. The discussion showed the deep attachment of the inhabitants to this truly special environment. We know that in heavy downpours the style of hedge-laying holds the water back and restrains the mountain torrent Drac from becoming swollen, that the preservation of the hedge is the best protection against the wind. But there remain fewer and fewer traces of the former customs, of the times when the trees were pruned so that gradually only pollarded tree trunks with a few branches at the top remained. Thus the secret of this landscape derives from a farming culture which cares about economy, usefulness, and the neighbour's opinion.

If today a tourist can enthuse over the channels and the paths in the ravines, if an ecologist can speak about biological diversity, if a group can stray away from their guide on the endlessly complicated paths, if a mountain toad can still thrive in the ponds, this is thanks to the habits that have been preserved from generation to generation.

But nothing indicates that it will be possible in the future to follow and supervise this continuity: the development of urbanization and industrialized agriculture, and outside influences are leaving their mark on the environment.

The comparison of conditions in Champsaur with those in the Virgental valley (in the Hohe Tauern massif in Austria) has shown how great an economic significance such an inheritance from the past can have. A farmer who engages in tourism as well as agriculture slowly begins to be aware of this inheritance but for efficiency's sake endeavours to balance the traditional and the newly acquired. Ever bigger lands are needed, still more modern farming equipment than the neighbour's, he mustn't "lag behind", ... and so on.

Without knowing the features of this special environment, without a close link with tourism, which uses such an image as a path through a ravine, without a worked-out policy, the enclosures will either be replaced by bigger fields or be gradually overgrown by trees and finally forest. A country park cannot assent to such banal development.

In getting to know the environment and protecting it, a particular culture is necessary. The farmer of the past ought to live on in each present-day inhabitant, while he with his way of life, his building, and maintaining his environment will know how to preserve the values of his predecessors. In this time of globalization it will be difficult to convince people that life in these places means deciding for something totally different from life in the suburb of a big city or in some other valley.

Terraces in the Haute Romanche valley
For the traveller reeling from the bends and narrowly constructed road who hurries up along the valley of the River Romanche to the meadows on the Lautaret pass, this is just one of many valleys. But gazing down from the summit of La Meije on the little chapel in Le Chazelet, he is quite surprisingly made to think about people. The little villages situated high up, however picturesque they may be, would be nothing special without the terraces that surround them.

If we look from close at hand, we see that these are not "les restanques", Provençal barriers to shore up earth, a dry-stone wall as support for a small plot where things can be planted. Since the land has a steep gradient, a wall built of irregular stones, which are difficult to lay, is soon covered by soil and becomes a retaining wall. The ground above and below it is rarely level: this also slopes. A particular feature of the landscape is the lack of horizontal lines; La Meije with its marvellous north face seemingly stamps its surroundings with perpendicularity.

People settled quite early in this depression among the limestone rocks, in a sheltered spot below the crystalline mountain faces, and through centuries of toil developed agriculture well suited to the harsh climate - resistant cereals such as rye, potatoes, gardens and haymeadows, which make it possible to rear various domestic animals. More recent development between the two wars slowly allowed breeding of animals which need only a small working force. The terraces inherited from earlier generations mostly became meadows, as well as fields of clover. Thus the mosaic of green, yellow and brown areas of polyculture was lost, to be replaced by a graduated scale of green, from the tender green of regularly mown meadows to the yellow-brown colour on the banks. A cultural environment which greatly suits artists and photographers in autumnal or evening light.

A moment of wonderment that will remain for the visitor as a memory of these present here and of those from older times.

Our own, more imaginable history is considered by some to date from the end of the last, so-called Würm glacial period, when the Middle Stone Age began about 10,000 to 12,000 years ago. New visitors came along the streams and rivers into the Alps, more contemporary highlanders, the so-called mesolithic hunters and gatherers of fruits. For their summer dwellings they did not seek out caves, but arranged them in open, flat places. High little platforms in the shelter of large rocks, sunny positions near to water (by mountain lakes or streams) and a hinterland richly blessed with wild animals constituted the basic conditions for their summer settlements; in the winter they returned to the valleys and warmer places.

Interestingly, all mesolithic settlements, from the Vercors plateau above Grenoble, Freissinieres in Les Écrins, and the Italian Alpe Veglia and Monte Baldo to Hirschbichl in the Hohe Tauern and the Krn pastures in the Slovene Alps have a similar situation at approximately the same altitude, as if they were selected and decided on in accordance with some unwritten standard for settlements. Still more interesting are the artefacts, stone tools typical of the Stone Age (mesolithic, neolithic). From France to Slovenia they are fashioned in the same way, with the same shape and same usefulness; as if made by the same hands in some common central workshop. Modern farming implements are the same or similar everywhere in the Alps, but it is less comprehensible that this was the case 10,000 and 5000 years ago as well. Were there contacts between the highlanders from the Eastern and Western Alps and were mutual exchanges of knowledge as common as they are now?

The cultivating of the Alps – 5000 years of survival culture

The Late Stone Age or neolithic is equated with the first and so far the only important revolution in the history of the human race. The so-called neolithic revolution signified the commencement of agriculture and cultivating the Alps. Agriculture in its most original sense. The technology of our third millenium has invented artificial food and genetically altered caricatures of food, but healthy food, all the cereals that we know, vegetables and domesticated animals were the invention of the nutritional reversal in eating habits about 5000 to 6000 years ago. Cultivated fields and the first permanent settlements started to characterize Alpine valleys, while the first shepherds came to high-altitude pastures with their flocks and herds.

The Copper, Bronze and Iron Ages were a logical continuation of the admirable creativity of the neolithic spirit. Visitors different from shepherds also came to the mountain world: seekers of mineral ores, after them collectors and diggers or miners. The Alps acquired strategic significance because of salt, copper, silver, even gold (in the Hohe Tauern), iron and other ores, while ore-rich regions gave rise to numerous military conflicts between the Alpine countries.

The original meaning of the word "culture" derives from French and is connected with the earth: clearing, levelling the "wilderness" to form fertile ground, working the land, sowing, digging, ploughing, reaping. Nowadays we understand the

Roland Dellagiacoma

LANDSCAPES OF WINE ON THE SUNNY SIDE OF THE ALPS

༄

Most people spontaneously link the Alps – and quite rightly so – with mountain panoramas, a diversity of natural and cultural landscapes which take one's breath away. It is precisely this variety of visual impressions within a small space - a view from the valley of high mountains, a countryside in which small patches of farmland alternate with mixed forest, and soaring above the whole mosaic the majestic silhouettes of peaks – that enthuses the crowds of tourists.

Anyone travelling over the Brenner or Reschen pass to the southern side of the main Alpine chain, at the altitude of the towns of Brixen or Schlanders, will catch sight of the attractive landscape of vineyards, which forms a total contrast to snow-covered summits. Two zones in this richly blessed land of wine come together in the Bolzano basin and the viticultural region then extends further along both sides of the Etsch (Adige) valley, across the terraced slopes of the upper Etsch valley while the best level positions for Pinot Nero are found as far as Salorno, the most southerly place in the Autonomous Province of Bozen/Bolzano in South Tyrol (also known as Alto-Adige).

In this region there flourish "Alpine wines with Mediterranean charm" (that's how the South Tyrolians advertise their wine) – a slogan which for once completely holds true. From the terraced vineyards in the village of Kortsch in the Vinschgau valley the view opens up to the glaciers of the Ortler group, while in the Eisack (Isarco) valley and from Bolzano there is an entrancing sight of the fascinating Dolomites with the Geisler group, the great massif of Schlern (2662 m) and Rosengarten (3002 m) glowing in the evening rays of the sun.

We ought not to deny that there are excellent native wines also beyond South Tyrol, in other Alpine countries: from the Savoy Alps with the red varietal Mondeuse to Wallis with its aromatic Dôle wine on the steep slopes of the Rhône, Ticino with its slightly dry Merlot, the elegant Pinot Nero (Blauburgunder) in the Graubünden region, some rareties in the Italian valley of Aosta and the highly concentrated "Sfursat", prepared in the Valtellina Alpine valley from the ripest semi-dry Chiavenasca (Nebbiolo) grapes.

But nowhere else except in South Tyrol are there so many different varieties of wine in such a small area: over a distance of about 80 km and a surface area of approximately 5000 hectares, at altitudes ranging from 200 to 1000 metres, there are over 20 native varieties of grape, which ferment into local specialities, from the Vernatsch (Schiava) table wine or the Lagrein variety with its rich flavour, to premium wines of international standing for wine snobs and lovers of labels. Natural factors, different kinds of soil, the microclimate, the topography, together with viticulturists and wine cellar specialists, all contribute to the wine its unique "terroir". In the last analysis this is what gives a wine or a region its special value: uniqueness, authenticity, difference, individual character, sensuous quality. Lovers of wine are almost always lovers of a region as well – because so many things link a wine with its region. Wine-tasting is like experiencing a region: consciously recognizing the aroma, the play of colours, the depth and breadth, the microclimate, and yet this does not suffice for the ultimate awareness of the complexity, mystique and poetry of wine or of the region as a whole. There is

still scope enough for exciting discussions about the best wines and the ideal region.

Just like the region, wine also has its own history. The oldest data go back to Georgia, 6000 BC, while in the Mediterranean world the vine (vitis vinifera) was systematically cultivated as early as 1600 BC. There is proof for the 2500-year-old existence of vineyards in what is now South Tyrol and Roman emperors valued Rhaetian wine, which was not preserved here in goatskins and clay amphoras but in wooden casks sheathed with iron bands. In the 8th century there were monasteries in Bavaria, Swabia and Austria that produced "bozenaere" and "traminer".

What is it that makes South Tyrol, its wine and regions so special? The Alpine and Mediterranean climates meet right here, giving warm days and fresh nights, and consequently big diurnal temperature variations, all of which contributes to the outstanding quality of white wines in particular. There is a different geology here, from the primeval rocks in the Eisack and Vinschgau valleys, the moraine soils in the upper Etsch valley, the "warm" porphyry underlying the best locations for the Lagrein variety in Bozen to the weathered limestone and dolomite rock in the southernmost part of the wine-producing regions of South Tyrol.

The soil contains minerals that give the wines their special salty and juicy flavour, the Alpine climate guarantees fine aromas and well-balanced acidity values, which ensures great satisfaction in drinking, while the wine does not have the over-strong taste that results from a high alcohol content. In addition to Mediterranean varietals such as Pinot Nero (Blauburgunder), Pinot Grigio (Rülander), Chardonnay, Riesling, Sauvignon Blanc, Merlot and Cabernet Sauvignon, their own special varietals grow in the wine-producing regions of South Tyrol, such as Müller-Thurgau, Sylvaner, Veltliner, Kerner, and the golden Muscat Ottonel.

There are three autochthonous varieties that represent the "USP" (Unique Selling Proposition) in this predominantly wine-growing country: the bright ruby red, aromatic and mild Vernatsch, the dark pomegranate red, somewhat coarse Lagrein with its full-bodied flavour, and the straw-yellow, aromatic Traminer, which originates from the showcase wine-growing village of Tramin.

A final thought about the common characteristics of an authentic region and authentic wine. There is here a vivid contrast to the worldwide levelling, popularization and uniformity of places, architecture, lifestyles and mass tastes - also where wine is concerned.

And less is more; quality as against quantity. Just as we cannot excessively exploit the cultural bounty of a region without it suffering irreparable damage, so also a big harvest and outstanding quality do not go together in the sphere of viticulture. It is only by consistently restricting the quantity, using natural methods of tending vineyards and natural cellaring that we can produce premium wines. Wine is the product of a specific region, it harnesses the cooperation of man and nature.

Your good health...!

word "cultivating" to mean maintaining and caring for already cultivated areas.

Culture in the Alps is synonymous with respect for the gifts of the earth, respect for natural laws and natural balance, a constant adapting to natural changes and confronting natural disasters that destroy the fertile land already gained.

Cultivating the Alps was not the activity we understand today but a merciless challenge and ceaseless struggle for survival in brutal conditions not to be compared with conditions in the valleys below the Alps.

The 5000-year-old culture in the Alps is a survival culture – that of agriculture. The carriers of this culture were the most persistent, the most inventive, the most adaptable, the strongest. It was a culture that knew no pity, no consolation, no idleness. Those who survived were the most resistant, the most experienced and most tested. Natural selection was merciless. It is still like that with the birds today.

The first settlers began literally from nothing. Archaeological excavations have confirmed a permanent and dense colonization 3000 years ago, during the late Bronze Age and Early Iron Age (Hallstatt), a period of successful agriculture, presumably peaceful, and so suitable for creativity. Experts place the first written documents of our distant ancestors in the Bronze Age. Symbols carved in rocks, rock engravings, are coded messages of an unknown civilization that was spiritually, culturally and materially highly developed. Most of them are in the valley Val Camonica (over 40,000) and on the high plateau La Vallée des Merveilles (at least 30,000 engravings) below the mountain Mont Bego in the Maritime Alps; among the best known are still more in Valtellina, on the Carschena plateau in the canton of Graubünden and somewhat later ones under the Dachstein mountains.

We can justifiably conclude that these rock engravings were made during peaceful and creative centuries, when people, after their daily work was done, still found time, pleasure and the need to carve images in rock from their everyday life, stylized figures of people, domesticated animals, tools and weapons, sketches of their dwellings. We do not know who were the master carvers of these artistically accomplished graphic symbols.

The cultivation of Alpine areas and reshaping of the relief was not only the result of farming and pasturing livestock. From the "metal" ages up to the beginning of the modern era the appearance of the high mountains was altered primarily because of mining. First for salt, then for copper, after which iron assumed first place and retained it until the 19th century. For a long time, salt was a strategic commodity, needed for food and preserving agricultural products (cheese, meat). The regions with salt mines in the Eastern Alps were some of the richest; proof of this prosperity is seen in the Hallstatt culture. But the discovery of iron, i.e. the birth of iron-forging or black magic, that new wizardry and skill which was able to charm iron out of apparently brown stone (such is iron ore) and fire, ended the advantage held by salt and gold. Both could be bought with iron; its strategic significance has lasted for 3000 years. From iron, not from gold, implements for cultivating the land were made, and weapons for conquering the world and destroying the culture of enemies.

Collecting iron ore on the surface, digging for it and mining in underground tunnels high up in the mountains have left remains that are still visible today: heaps of tailings, round hollows on the surface, a dense network of stone-paved pack routes. The worst consequences of iron manufacture were changes in the vegetation. To smelt iron ore, enormous quantities of wood and charcoal were required. In the last three thousand years, the Alpine forests were relentlessly felled several times over in the interests of charcoal-making and woodcutting. The natural renewal of forests lasted from one to two hundred years, until they were felled again. Seen from our present-day viewpoint, such merciless exploitation by no means meant "cultivating" the Alps, but their harsh, irresponsible and un-cultural destruction. Only in the 14th century were the first forestry and mining regulations issued, which prevented such violence.

The real, permanent inhabitants of the high mountains were not shepherds but miners. The word "miner" in French and German means a man from the mountain, a man of the mountains, a highlander. Some of today's Alpine pastures and shepherd settlements developed from what were originally miners' dwelling places. Mountain pasturing, especially dairy-farming, was essential for supplying miners every day with milk, which was the main sustenance in the mountains up to the modern period.

The settlement of the Alps

Settlement was the last phase of cultivating the Alps. There are various theories as to how waves of settlers came from all directions and pressed upwards along the rivers to reach the highest valleys. Experts distinguish between the particularities of Germanic and Romance settlement, but have forgotten about the Slavonic settlement of the Eastern Alps as well as the aborigines, the original and oldest inhabitants of the Alps. The names of mountains and rivers and numerous archaic relics in today's languages are assumed to be a tradition handed down by the Celts, Veneti, Rhaetians, Carnians; we simply do not know what names they used for themselves. Scientific theories about our prehistoric ancestors in the Alps contradict each other. Mere uncritical repetition of unproved assertions and superficial copying of theories lacks interest.

The Romance type of settlement spread from the southern and western sides of the Alps. It followed the rivers which flow into the Mediterranean and halted below the ridges beyond which the waters flow into the North Sea and Black Sea. The characteristics of Romance settlement are terrace cultivation, stock-breeding on shared mountain pastures and typical compact valley settlements with unique, virtuoso stone architecture.

The Germanic type of settlement spread from the northern and partly north-eastern sides. Unlike the compact Romance villages on the southern side, the northern settlement was characterized by scattered hamlets and solitary mountain farms, which from a distance remind one of eagles' nests, perched on almost impossibly steep slopes. Stock-breeding, forests, cultivated fields in incredibly steep positions, economic self-suffiency, great individuality and pride in their farms, and wooden architecture are the particular features of this settlement.

The Slavonic settlement type on the eastern and south-eastern sides of the Alps shows an intermingling of characteristics of Romance, Germanic and aboriginal kinds of settlement. Settlers in the valleys of the Eastern Alps are known for their more up-to-date farming methods and from the early Middle Ages they maintained the mining and iron-manufacture traditions. Farms and settlements on the northern sides are similar to the Germanic ones, while the architecture on the southern Mediterranean side, from the compact valley hamlets to the scattered mountain farms and shepherd settlements, has a marked Mediterranean character. In the Karavanke, the Savinja Alps and on the Pohorje massif, a special settlement type has been preserved to the present day: the so-called *celci* – the largest self-sufficient farms in the Alps. These estates, ranging from 200 to 400 hectares, mostly consisting of forest and rocky terrain above the tree-line, represent a special feature in the Alps on account of their size, while at the same time they are the highest farms in the Eastern Alps.

The difference between the northern and southern settlement of the Alps can be briefly and simply characterized as a culture of wood on the northern side and a culture of stone on the Mediterranean side.

The alpine cultural landscape

Only a good forty years ago did the cultural landscape become a concept for the recognizability, identity and mutual differentiation of individual countries, including the Alpine ones.

The Alpine "cultural landscape" reflects the diversity of man's work on the land from cultivation and settlement to different uses of the ground, it is a testimony to human culture in changing the natural environment and an open book displaying millenia of experience in adapting to the laws of Alpine nature. The expression is modern and full of nostalgia for the classical image of the Alpine landscape, which has been changing and even disappearing over the last fifty years.

The aesthetic evaluation of the cultivated Alpine countryside is appreciated only by visitors. Those who worked the land did not see any particular beauty in the fruits of their laborious toil, apart from satisfaction that the work was done. Just as the pearl shell oyster with pain and extreme efforts extrudes its pearl, without seeing it or knowing it is there, so too the beauty and creation of the Alpine cultural landscape are linked with exertion, pain, exhaustion and life-threatening danger, but those who created it were not aware of it.

The cultural landscape did not come about through the plans of landscape architects, but unawares, spontaneously, in a strictly rational and coldly functional way. This is a permanent process carried on by numerous generations and anonymous master-craftsmen. In more recent times, the cultural landscape has been valued as a common cultural heritage, as something for the public good, and its preservation as being in the public interest.

Turning the land into terraces is the oldest farming culture. In Alpine valleys, terraces with meadows and cultivated fields can be seen as a distant echo of the incredibly complicated rice terraces in the Himalayas. Nowadays on the remnants of the oldest settlement and its age-old farming, cultivated fields have been exchanged for monoculture meadows – due to changes in agricultural methods – while even more terraced areas have been abandoned and are overgrown.

The most beautiful monuments to the cultivation of the Alps and the cultural landscape are the stony terraces on steep moraines in the valleys of Wallis, Aosta, Valtelina, in Liguria and Piedmont, and in the South Tyrol between Brixen/ Bressanone and Bozen/Bolzano. These terraces are a show gallery of viticulture and inventiveness, revealing how level patches for vines have been snatched from the bare and steep rocky slopes. Two pearls, unique symphonies of the cultural landscape, are Wallis, a veritable oasis among alpine glaciers, and the terraces in Liguria, covered with vineyards at an altitude of 1300 m and plantations of olive trees. The terrace culture on the southern side of the Alps is a paean to this art in stone; a special beauty radiates from it, and it breathes the spirit of an original culture.

A particular feature of cultivating the Alps are mountain farms, scattered high above the valleys of Carinthia, the Salzburg region, the Tyrol and from the Dolomites to the French Alps. The homesteads with their modest fields and meadows literally attached to precipitous slopes are striking evidence of the indomitable will to survive in conditions of impossible terrain.

Due to changes in agriculture and the abandonment of some forms of farming in the 1960s and 1970s and the parallel incursion of mass tourism with aspects opposed to the environment, the cultural landscape began to change and lose the adjective "cultural". The introduction of meadow monocultures for intensive animal husbandry in flat valley regions, ignorance of and disdain for the natural equilibrium, migration and emptying of highland settlements, the expansion in traffic and leisure-time activities, as well as anarchic building projects have impoverished the alpine countryside and robbed it of its cultural identity. This altered cultural landscape no longer has the ecological function of preserving bio-diversity; with the neglect of measures for restraining flood waters and measures against natural disasters, the function of maintaining the natural equilibrium has been lost also in residential areas.

LIFE IN THE ALPS – FARMING IN THE MOUNTAINS, SURVIVAL CULTURE

According to the definition in a special decree passed by the Tyrolean provincial government, the status of a mountain farmer belongs to those who farm above 1200 m and those whose farm is situated at an altitude of at least 500 m. Typical features of mountain farming are poor access routes and the steepness of the cultivated land.

Farming in the Alps cannot be compared with farming in the lowland areas of Europe, since working conditions in and among the mountains are far harder than conditions in the plains.

Life in the Alps, just like that by the Mediterranean, has two different faces. The first is seen by satisfied holiday-makers, who lie and sunbathe on the terraces of Alpine hotels, smiling hikers and cyclists, and bored tourists lacking ideas about

how to spend their free time. The other face is unknown to visitors, nor does it interest them.

We must not evaluate and interpret life in the Alps nostalgically. The so-called Alpine idyll does not exist and never did. It is a product of an external view of the Alps. This misleading image was created by those who did not live in the Alps and therefore did not experience the dark side of daily life in the mountains. They concocted a mosaic of what is beautiful and pleasing, but with the eyes of city folk and visitors. The reality is preserved in old photographs: husbands and wives bent and hidden under huge piles of hay on their heads, women yoked to a plough, which they pull up steep slopes, men in extremely dangerous rock faces, over which they build wooden chutes for a daily supply of water, old, young and children's faces of both sexes that were buried under avalanches, mourners on narrow paths heading for a graveyard several hours away, searching out and collecting fertile soil at the foot of steep fields and carrying it back up in big baskets, several generations of one family gathered round their common table for a poor meal. In this hard daily round there was no time for illness. Yet despite the unfriendly reality, the people in the photographs are laughing and radiate an incredible will to live. A pride which does not know how to and does not want to make a request to anybody, though all are in need of help.

On account of the cold climate, only the most resistant crops could grow in Alpine fields: beans, cabbage, potato and buckwheat, of cereals just rye and barley. The old variety of potato, adapted to a mountain environment, has practically died out; similarly horsebean, the oldest kind of fat bean. The food was very modest, but for this reason very healthy. Chestnuts were an important source for survival.

Bringing in timber was connected with numerous accidents. Not only in steep forests with difficult access, but also in turbulent rivers along which they floated logs – with exceptional skill and courage – to the nearest roads, many unfortunate

victims died. The owners of forests acknowledged the forest must never be sold; it was the last reserve for potentially difficult times.

In comparison with the poverty in mountainous regions, the sunny terraces with their vineyards, olive groves and fertile fields on the southern side of the Alps are like a dreamy vision from another world.

About 150 years ago, the Alps were a symbol of dire poverty. Especially villages in western Piedmont, in Tyrol, Trentino, Carnia, Friuli and the Soča river basin. Poor harvests, over-population, and too little food produced gave rise to famine and emigration. The exodus from the Alps occurred in several waves. The first, in the second half of the 19th century, drove the hungry and desperate to the USA. Those who left were the young, the strong and the most capable, leaving behind older and incapacitated people, who could not manage the farms by themselves. Less food, less hay and fewer animals only aggravated the famine. Uncultivated fields and neglected meadows were the first consequences of the exodus. There was also much seasonal emigration. A moving chapter in this story of poverty was the children sent from the Tyrol to make the long journey on foot over snowbound passes to look for work in more well-to-do places. *Schwabenkinder*, as these pitiful ones were called, represent a sad tale of survival. Actually, many of them died on the way, due to the ardours of the journey, the cold and malnutrition.

The number of inhabitants in the Eastern Alps was greatly reduced during the First World War, when two million men and boys fell on the front line between Trieste, the Julian and Carnian Alps and the Dolomites as far as Ortler. A fatal flu epidemic after this war and the accompanying famine caused a new exodus from the Alps. The final wave of emigrants emptied the Alpine villages after the Second World War, when the big cities needed an unlimited working force for their renewal and new development.

The migrationary wave today goes in the opposite direction. Because summer and winter tourism is increasing, there is a growing number who move to Alpine settlements from elsewhere. The social structure has changed. Along with modern tourism come banks, agencies and property speculators. Mountain farms are also different: there is no longer self-sufficient farming, but a livelihood is provided by complementary tourist activities with the renovation of old buildings for tourist rooms and holiday flats. Farmers and their family members become managers of restaurants and hotels, ski instructors and cable car workers, tourist and mountain guides, salesmen and employees who travel to work every day. Inventive and successful local initiatives have found a niche for marketing the health-giving bounty of the Alps and offer employment to those living in the vicinity.

In spite of the relatively high standards, the most up-to-date farm mechanization, the good road connections to the furthest solitary farms, and in spite of the information and communication networks, there are still regions in the Alps where you can meet young people, both men and women, who in summer pass surprised tourists as they carry heavy baskets on their backs, piled high with firewood collected from the forest.

Transhumance, pasture culture and the stock-breeding year

In the past millenium a particular type of pasture culture has developed in the Alps: the stock-breeding year or the pasture cycle. In a metaphorical sense it is also transhumance, i.e. the moving of animals in several stages into the mountains, and the alternation of pastures according to a definite time sequence.

The stock-breeding year begins afresh each spring when grazing animals are moved from the valley villages to the lower or haymeadow alps, from where they are driven to the high alps at the end of June, when they have grazed the first grass. There the shepherds tend the animals and make cheese until autumn. The frost and first snow of September drive both animals and shepherds back to the lower pastures. Here the former must survive until November, when snowfall makes them return to the valley to overwinter and then this cycle begins again in the spring.

Since there was not enough pasturage for all in the mountains, an unwritten "pasture order" gradually came into existence, based on experience. Pasture rights were strictly allocated: for individual villages, individual farms, for each type of animal in particular and at set times. The fundamental rule was that individual farmers could use the common alps to graze only as many animals as they could feed at home during the winter. This fodder was prepared in summer when they made hay in the valley meadows and on the lower alps. This simple rule meant that all the meadow areas were carefully mown, cleared and constantly maintained. The "pasture order", the basis of summer life and husbandry on the alps, was a unique code of work discipline, work morale, common obligations, a strict division of work and rights and of social justice. This pasture culture developed gradually. Transhumance is what remains of the medieval nomadic migration of flocks and shepherds, lasting for some days or some weeks, from dry Mediterranean places to pastures below the mountains. Today transhumance is an accepted concept for the whole-day moving of sheep from the southern part of the Alps across high passes and glaciers to the rich Alpine pastures on the northern side.

The best-known example of such migration is in Tyrol, where every year farmers from the South Tyrolean valley of Schnalstal

(Italy) drive their sheep over a high saddle and the Jochferner Glacier and then down towards North Tyrol (Austria) to the pastures above the Ötztal valley. Beside this ancient route, at an altitude of 3210 m, near the Tisenjoch, the remains of so far the oldest man in the Alps were found in 1991, preserved in the glacier for 5300 years. This was "Ötzi" or the Iceman, as he later came to be called. This archaeological find stimulated systematic research into prehistoric pasturing in the high mountains. Prior to 1991 everyone was convinced that Alpine regions between 1600 m and 3200 m had no prehistoric remains worth mentioning. Ötzi contributed to a new flurry of research through the entire range of the Alps. Surprising finds have proved that the pasture culture of the Alps is at least 5000 years old. Was Ötzi a shepherd, pilgrim, refugee or a shaman operating beneath the Tyrolean sacred mountain of Similaun, which rises immediately above the Tisenjoch?

The result of this 5000-year-old pasture culture is cheese. Many respectfully call it the white gold of the Alps. Made from the milk of cows, sheep, goats, ordinary, special and unique cheeses. Nobody knows how many different kinds there are in the Alps. Not only each Alpine region, even each village, each farm, each alp has its own special cheeses. Even two cheese dairies on the same alp do not make identical cheeses. The preparation of the best, the most sought-after and the most expensive cheeses is knowledge carefully guarded, accessible only to the most experienced, capable and chosen cheese-makers. Each cheese has hidden in it experience, traditional knowledge, new technology and ancient culture.

Many old fairytales talk about cheese, with stories of the surprises our ancestors had whenever they encountered giants from other time dimensions high up in the mountains. These giants were supposed to have taught people how to keep milk so that it did not spoil and how cheese is made.

More modern cheese-making is documented in the second half of the 19th century, when the first dairy and cheese-making courses were introduced in the Alps. In this period the Austro-Hungarian authorities invited cheese-making experts from Switzerland to teach their new technology on the pastures of the Carnian and Julian Alps. Similarly, individuals from the Julian Alps were enabled to go to Switzerland to obtain cheese-making knowledge. How cheese was made in antiquity and still earlier we do not know (as yet). Undoubtedly they did prepare it, although great copper vessels heated over an open hearth - the trademark of old cheese dairies on the alps - were not yet known. In the Julian Alps an oral tradition has been preserved about the ancient way of preparing cheese when there were no metal vessels in which milk could be heated over a fire. According to this tradition milk was heated, conserved and then gradually made into cheese by placing hot stones in wooden tubs, and then pouring the milk over them.

The array of different Alpine cheeses on the market is becoming unmanageable. Private cheese-makers and their associations with trademarks and controlled provenance compete successfully with big producers of world-famous cheeses. The biodiversity on mountain pastures has a significant influence on the quality of cheese. Boutique home production is not the same as production in factories with state-of-the-art technology. Unfortunately, highly regarded cheeses, bearing well-known Alpine trademarks, are appearing in big shopping centres, but have been produced in countries far from the Alps. Where have correctness and authenticity been lost?

THE ALPINE NATIONS AND THEIR CULTURAL IDENTITY

The cultural heritage and cultural tradition

How many Alpine nations and ethnic groups are there? The answer is not simple and depends on who is asked and how tolerant he/she is towards the national and linguistic diversity in the Alps. Counting nations and ethnic groups is a tricky business, and can even be unjust to those involved. So this topic is deliberately omitted, as it is not necessary to weigh down a book which has borrowed the symbol of birds for the understanding of the Alps.

Counting Alpine languages is also a thankless task, especially for the unacknowledged ones from the standpoint of the acknowledged ones. Everyone's mother tongue is an elementary human value, a divine gift and a marvel of creation for expression, communication and showing emotion. Why deny and denigrate the languages of others? If different languages were not necessary, they would not exist.

There are at least ten Alpine languages. Let us start in a simple way: French, German, Italian, Slovene and also Rhaeto-Romance in Switzerland have the status of national languages. In Italy Ladin and Friulian are also acknowledged, while the Occitanian and Provençal languages in the Western Alps are scarcely acknowledged, and the unacknowledged Walliser language of Switzerland would be the tenth. But there remain proud ethnic groups from the Maritime Alps, Liguria and Savoy to Carnia. Which language have they inherited? Their own or a dialect of neighbouring language groups? Disregarded linguistic relics of the original inhabitants are preserved in toponyms and oronyms. Some names of rivers and mountains have the same meaning in different languages within the arc of the Alps: Isar, Isère, Isel, Islitz/Izlica, Isarco, Enns, Adige, Nadiža, Bela, Belca, Belica, Plagne, Planja, Planina, Planica, Plân, Karwendel, Kras, Karavanke, Carnia, Carniola, Carinthia, Sele, Sella, Söl, Pic, Pez, Petsch, Peč, Špik.

The cultural heritage

Professionally, there is a distinction between the material and non-material heritage. The latter is also termed the cultural tradition. The cultural heritage consists of the material, tangible and visible remains of our ancestors. Everything that is the work of human hands and everything that marks off one individual region from another, everything different, varied, special, unique.

The architectural heritage is the most noticeable element in every landscape. Each place has its own special characteristics that are seen at first glance. The Alpine arc is a highly complex mosaic of construction diversity. From the two basic materials, wood and stone, to original combinations of both, from gently slanting to steep roofs, from wooden shingles or stone tiles to bricks or straw. The culture of stone is rational and inventive, stone architecture is marvellously ensconced in its environment. The culture of wood makes possible virtuoso construction and decorative qualities, wooden architecture provides warmth and safety in case of earthquakes.

The cultural heritage of the Alps is a pan-European gallery displaying the creativity of anonymous masters. Architecture without architects. What inventiveness and brilliant adaptability the builders of little cluster villages on hill-tops in the Maritime Alps, Liguria or above the Aosta valley had at their finger-tips. Nobody knows who built them, we only know they were built without urban plans and without designs for each house individually. Similarly, we do not know who were the artists that created a poetry of stone in the mountain villages of western Piedmont, in the Stura valley, in Tessino and the remote valleys of Lombardy or who hewed wooden masterpieces in Wallis and the Eastern Alps. Who sketched the urbanism of Soglio and who constructed the mighty stone-built and painted houses in the Engadine villages? We do not know the master-builders of the shepherd settlements in the Eastern Alps, nowadays declared to be cultural monuments; the creators of the typical Bovec-Trenta house are not recorded anywhere – this has become a classic example of building that is extremely economical in terms of energy.

Years ago Luigi Demateis systematically collected the architectural particularities of the Alps. He wrote and published 40 books on the typical architecture of farmhouses in individual Alpine regions. His life's work, in photographs and sketches, represents a unique documentation of diversity in construction. Demateis started in good time to capture and preserve in photography a disappearing heritage. Many houses from his opus no longer exist. Due to the strong urbanization of old settlements and the disdain of present-day construction aggression, the Alps are losing their cultural face. New blocks of flats and big office buildings are the same everywhere in Europe, they have no personal face, no soul. Will they last at least fifty years?

The cultural tradition or non-material heritage has a spiritual dimension. What we feel and hear and what is placed in our memory. A building in the cultural heritage can be private property, but the cultural tradition is universal and the property of all. No folksong is the property of the singer and no legend is the property of the narrator. The non-material heritage is a tradition of the beautiful, the noble, the authentic: different languages and dialects, customs, songs, music and dance, myths, legends and fairytales, old and well-tried forms of knowledge and behaviour, historical memory. This intangible wealth cannot be sold or stolen, but it can be copied, re-experienced, presented, described, recorded, also despised and forgotten.

Just like the Alpine cultural landscape, the cultural tradition, too, along the whole range of the Alps is changing, losing its authentic and archaic character. Old customs are lost in folklore caricatures and kitschy tourist events, adapted to poor taste and the ignorance of the audience.

The common cultural identity of the Alps

All the wealth of diversity described in the previous sections, from settlement characteristics and the cultural landscape to pasture culture and the cultural heritage, hides in its background common roots, a common identity. The song rendered with feeling by a women's choir from a Ligurian or Occitanian village is similar in its melody to a song that women sing in some highland place in the Slovene Alps or in the Hohe Tauern. Although the language and content are different, we know from the melodic character that the song belongs somewhere in the Alps. It is the same with folk music and dances, with costumes and the culture of dressing. An echo of the landscape is captured in the melodies: in valleys among the mountains you sense the ready wit, which is different from the pastoral echoes in undulating landscapes where the high Alps fade away into the level plains of big rivers.

In old photographs of everyday peasant life, people's faces and clothes are the same, regardless of whether the motif derives from the western or eastern part of the Alpine chain.

Myths and Alpine legends, customs, thanksgiving hymns, feast-days and the annual repetition of ancient ceremonies and celebrations do not differ in content in different Alpine countries, the tradition of common ancestors is handed down only in languages that differ.

The similar culture of food - similar produce and products, similar preparation, conserving and preserving of bread, cheese, meat and fruit – is also a common characteristic.

The differences are shared, the equality of those differences represents a shared culture.

The millenial experiences of survival, healthy pride and a lack of trust in anything that has come from elsewhere, a deeply emotional attachment to the earth, to their home and locality, patriotic awareness, an admirable care to preserve their mother tongue, making pilgrimages to sacred mountains, respecting the tradition of their ancestors and a sensibility towards their personal identity are shared features of the Alpine nations and our common identity. Isn't it strange that nobody has ever thought of the United States of the Alps?

SACRED MOUNTAINS, MYTHS AND LEGENDS

The Alpine world was always divided into that above, sacrosanct and inviolable, and that below, earthly and secular. Below, civilizations were born that created and developed a special economic and residential culture. But the high mountains were a world of demons, dragons, treasures and gardens of paradise, fables and legends, bewitched snakes, white and shining fairies, crystal palaces, great cities that had disappeared and were hidden under glaciers, a place of unimaginable leaps into other dimensions of time and space, a meeting-point between the real and the incomprehensible, a barren, dangerous and yet hallowed world. Also inviolable, where a human being did not know how to, did not hope to and was not allowed to enter. In our subconsciousness this realm above remained a mystery and a sanctuary.

According to ancient tradition a sacred mountain is a symbolic place where sky and earth meet, a sanctuary and the centre of the world. A place for pilgrimages, worship and spiritual experience.

Through long millenia man anchored his horizons of the spirit, his longings, dreams and desires in symbolic sacred mountains. The high mountains always warned him that far above them or deep within them, indeed above the loftiest peak and beneath the deepest abyss, anywhere and everywhere, there was a great mystery, the boundary of the permissible, the boundary of our capacities, and the boundary of final knowledge.

Sacred mountains are known in all the mountain ranges of the world and every nation that lives below mountains has its own sacred one. But the Alps have the greatest number. The Alps with their mountain chains and high plateaus together constitute one single symbolic sanctuary with a dense network of prehistoric cult sites and sacred places at great heights. In the last two centuries the Alpine nations in strengthening their own identity have started to call their highest summits sacred mountains: Mont Blanc, Monte Viso, Similaun, Bernina, Ortler, Grossglockner, Triglav. Each of these is enwrapped with its own myth and legend. But sacred mountains in the real meaning of the word are only those where remains have been found of old sacrificial sites, a kind of open shrine in the open air: Rochemelon/Rocciamelone (3538 m), the highest cult site in Europe – this favourite sacred mountain between France and Italy still attracks numerous pilgrims from both countries every year. Another example is Schlern (2563 m), the sacred mountain of South Tyrol.

A particular feature of the undulating landscape between the Mediterranean and the Alps, from Piedmont to Slovenia, is the striking lower mountains, seen from a distance, with their pilgrimage churches, situated in pre-Christian cult locations. The majority are in the Eastern Alps: South Tyrol, Ost Tyrol and Nord Tyrol, Friuli, Carinthia, Styria and all of Slovenia. In Slovenia some of them are called literally Sveta gora (Sacred Mountain).

Sacred mountains in the Alps are sanctuary and cult relics, where the pre-Christian spiritual tradition was built on and continued with Christian content: Mont Thabor, Col d' Iseran and Notre Dame des Voirons in Savoy, Sant'Anna di Vinadio (2010 m) and San Magno in Piedmont, Tartscher Büchel at the crossroads of the Rhaeto-Romance, Romance and Germanic cultures, the South Tyrolean St. Verena on Ritten and St. Hippolyte on Glaiten, San Romedio in Trentino, Weissenstein in Tyrol, Monte Santo di Lussari at the crossroads of the Slovene, Friulian and German cultures, Magdalensberg and Dobratsch (called Sacred Stone in the Middle Ages) in Carinthia, three Sveta goras in Slovenia, Mariazell in Styria, Sonntagberg in Lower Austria; those listed are only the best known.

We are justified in assuming that the spiritual world of the prehistoric inhabitants of the Alps was very closely linked with the mysterious sacred mountains. Today's pilgrimages and mass outings to pilgrimage churches in the mountains reflect a tradition going back for some millenia. A very persistent, very deep and direct tradition. The popular annual processions of pilgrims from one valley over mountains and passes into another valley (e.g. in Piedmont, the Salzburg region and Carinthia) give evidence of the unusual inveteracy of this spiritual dimension of mountains.

The worship and cult of stone, especially of some enormous, solitary rocks, the worship of water and sacred springs, the worship of trees, so-called places of power and energy, pre-Christian cult stones, built in beneath the altars of Christian churches, undecipherable messages in art, engraved in granite walls in Val Camonica or in the valley below Mont Bego (meaning God's Mountain), menhirs and circles of huge stone blocks and votive cairns on passes and saddles are remnants of megalithic culture, which left permanent traces in the Alps. Probably we will never know the true function of the assumed sun temple on top of the Little St Bernard pass (2188 m), where a magnificent view of the highest sacred mountain of the Alps, Mont Blanc, opens up from the centre of a stone circle. We can still only guess what the builders of the megalithic complex Kaser above the village of Vent in the Ötztal valley wanted to declare.

Myths and legends about gods and heroes from the high mountains, about the creation of the world, about crystal palaces beneath glaciers, about the destruction of the world and the hope of a new world that will arise from the present one constitute a majestic message about the disdained sanctity and inviolability of the Alps. Also a warning and a reminder.

Legends and fairytales in all the languages of the Alps resemble each other in content and conceal a disturbing message of how irresponsible human intervention in sensitive mountain ecosystems can destroy the natural balance. Such a symbolic content is found in the Zlatorog fairytale, about a white chamois with golden horns, who guarded a gold treasure in inaccessible mountains above heavenly beautiful gardens. The fairytale was written down in the Julian Alps, but its variants are also known in the Central Alps. The background of the story is the inviolability of what is most beautiful and most valuable in Alpine nature. Human lust for wealth, violation of the inviolable, the forbidden, of natural laws triggers the destruction of the mountain and man's death in the abyss. But nature recovers and re-establishes its order, yet without man. A very modern fairytale, which makes one think.

TRAFFIC

He who sows roads reaps traffic. This thought, which arose among the instigators of the Protocol on Traffic of the Alpine Convention, expressed a true picture of the traffic strategy in the Alps. Everywhere old roads have been widened and new ones built with the excuse that the existing state of affairs will thus be improved and road safety increased. But no widening and no new road has improved traffic conditions and road safety. Instead, as in a vicious circle, overburdened traffic, speed and danger have only increased.

The transit motorway corridors across and through the Alps, the passes and tunnels can barely swallow the traffic overload between Europe and the Mediterranean, between the eastern and western parts of Europe. It is in everybody's interests to cross the Alps as soon as possible, as quickly as possible, and by the shortest route possible. So the Alps are ensnared and turned into a concrete monster that less and less effectively digests the traffic currents and the traffic jams where vehicles crawl for hours.

Can this system burst apart? Or will it in self-defence trigger all sorts of avalanches, release rockfalls, devastating flood waters, and close and destroy roads? Enlightened individuals, initiatives by local citizens and environmental organizations call for people to sober up and take action. Appeals for heavy transit traffic across the Alps to be re-directed to the railways and for Alpine valleys to be closed to individual tourist vehicles do not reach the politicians who decide. Realistic solutions disappear with the banal conclusion that the railways are too out-of-date and worn-out to take over heavy transit traffic. This is true. Modernization of the Alpine railway network depends on a big cycle of investment that requires the willingness of all European nations to participate, and not only the Alpine nations directly affected. There are differing interests. Decisions are influenced by big lobbies which are far removed from the Alps and take no interest in the environmental problems of the Alpine region. Is the overpowerful road transport lobby in the background? Where is the decisive and far-sighted action of those who 100 and 150 years ago began to build the first railways and first tunnels through the Alps? And that was at a time when nobody even dreamt of today's crisis on overburdened roads.

Alpine passes, old trade routes and their historical significance

The first trans-European routes for merchants, packmen, pilgrims and armies led over Alpine passes and saddles. Only at first sight are the Alps an impassable barrier between the Mediterranean and Northern Europe. In actual fact, even the most closed Alpine valley has a passage somewhere high up leading to the other side. Valleys at the beginning of all the Alpine rivers on the south side have links with valleys at the beginning of rivers that flow down the northern or eastern side. Thus the Alps, when seen from a high altitude, appear like an immense but logically ordered blood circulation system, in which two hydrological systems meet on lofty ridges. Across the watershed between the North Sea (the Rhine), the Black Sea (the Danube, Inn, Drau/Drava, Mur/Mura, Enns and Sava rivers) and the Mediterranean (the Rhône with its tributaries from the French Alps, the Roya, Po, Adige, Piave, Tagliamento and Soča/Isonzo rivers) lie the best-known Alpine passes. Today's roads to the top of these saddles and crossing points wind along the traces of millenia-old shepherds' paths and later, narrow pack routes.

The lines of communication across the Alps are older than we imagine. Traces and packmen's relics from classical and prehistoric times and evidence of ancient connections over the Alps have been found alongside all the important crossings. We can only guess when and why people started to look for passages from one part of the Alps to another. The first settlers, who followed Alpine rivers upwards to the most hidden valleys, were forced for survival's sake to explore the unknown worlds beyond the ridges. At first hunters, afterwards shepherds with their flocks, then mineral ore prospectors and miners. The high passes were used by merchants, porters, packmen, smugglers and army deserters, pilgrims and impoverished farmers when they searched for new chances of survival in foreign places.

The three best-known articles of merchandise in old times gave rise to the names of the first trade routes across the Alps: amber, salt, iron. Amber, the gold of the Baltic Sea, as both jewellery and a miraculous curative stone, was transported along the amber routes between Adriatic and Baltic harbours. Salt from Alpine mines was exchanged for wine, oil and

spices from the Mediterranean. Of the salt routes, also called salt roads, the best-known were those from Ventimiglia in the Gulf of Liguria along Alpine ridges to Lac Léman and the crossing of the Eastern Alps from Venice to Hallstatt or Salzburg. The iron routes, known from antiquity for trading in iron products (also semi-maufactured), were used up to modern times, when the first railways were built.

The crossings from one linguistic, cultural and social environment to another broadened the horizons of knowledge, brought new experiences, the exchange of artisan skills, mutual cooperation and the intermingling of cultures. The echoes of distant regions reaching closed Alpine valleys also encouraged often deceptive dreams of a better and more beautiful world somewhere on the other side.

Nowadays we marvel at the boldness and ingenuity of those who widened dangerous paths above precipitous cliffs and through wild, barely passable gorges into pack routes and later into paved pack roads. Memorial chapels, crucifixes and votive wayside shrines, frequently encountered along old paths, hide shocking stories of people who met a tragic death at their work.

The valleys and villages below mountain passes were considered economically developed, since the local people had permanent sources of income thanks to packmen. Various artisans settled along the roads to care for horses and carts, travellers bought food for themselves and fodder for their pack animals; passes were also characterized by village inns with overnight accommodation for people and horses, while at the top of the pass there were shelters and hospices with healers and first aid.

The present-day roads for car traffic over Alpine passes represent a unique technical heritage and have become part of the Alpine identity. The best-known and the oldest road passes are: Lauterat and Montgènevre, Mont Cenis, Tende, the Great and Little St. Bernard passes, Maloja and Julier, Simplon and Bernina, Splügen and St. Gotthard, Stelvio/Stilfserjoch and Fuorn, Silvretta, Arlberg, Brenner, picturesque passes in the Dolomites, Hochtor, Vršič, Sölk, Ljubelj/Loibl. Some of them, with impossibly twisting serpentine bends, are sheer poetry of technical creativity, respectfully adapted to the mountain landscape, and also symbolizing man's insuperable will to cross over, to see the other side and come to know new worlds.

How much the rocks at the top could tell, if they knew how to speak! Before the advent of the car, when people had to struggle over on foot or with pack animals, the passes were places of human drama and tragedy. Nobody knows how many unfortunate people died in deep snow due to starvation, exhaustion and the cold, how many due to avalanches and blizzards, how many due to storms, lightning, fog and going astray. Many a wearied packman and pilgrim failed to reach the rest and warm safety of hospices and shelters that would have saved their lives. In those times, nobody except their relatives far away missed the dying wretches who did not make it over the top. The highest point of a pass was a place to give thanks for a successful journey. Also a place to offer sacrifices. The poor placed only a stone in gratitude; in this way stone cairns were formed on high crossings.

Today some passes have been altered beyond recognition into winter sports centres, in summer mostly closed artificial cities, hotels and apartment blocks like silos with no soul or identity.

TOURISM – THE GENIE OUT OF THE BOTTLE, A BLESSING OR A CURSE?

The Alps, as the birds see them today, are no longer the Alps of 150 years ago, when a new economic activity began: tourism. For long centuries famine, poverty and exodus were synonymous with life in the Alps. Tourism brought progress and a new mentality, new hope and expectations, new challenges, new possibilities for development, new areas of knowledge and contacts with the outside world, it enabled permanent employment at home and stable sources of income, it gradually improved living conditions and the quality of life for the Alpine population.

On the other hand, tourism in the last fifty years has completely changed the appearance and identity of the Alpine cultural landscape. Mass tourism, with summer and winter sport, has led to mountain relief being levelled out for ski slopes, car-parks and access roads, plus the unending explosion of new hotel and apartment complexes. From the air this resembles the uncontrollable, unearthly plasma of horror films, which sucks in the old town centres, typical architecture and characteristic appearance of the valleys. The comparative advantages and particularities of individual tourist areas are neglected: to have something that others do not have. New hotels in the Alps now do not differ from hotels by the sea. With rare exceptions, what is offered becomes uniform, unimaginative, supermarket-style.

The Alps simply are not necessary any more for Alpine tourism. Tourist entrepreneurs force their guests into wellness centres and aqua parks, while thermal spas are becoming a new tourist hit. Instead of a refreshing rest beside an alpine river or lake or below a waterfall, in fine viewspots, in the sun and fresh air, and instead of long walks through the forests, more and more tourists are pressed into spending a doubtful holiday break beneath air-conditioned glass domes above brimming swimming pools with stifling air and the typical smell of chlorinated water; in a countless throng, seekers after relaxation must follow various organizers and charlatan healers, under their baton they must like pliant sheep do exercises, perform weird movements, and meditations to order (!).

The beginnings and development of tourism

In the Alps tourism began at the end of the 18th and during the 19th centuries. At first as assistance, service and provision for explorers (especially botanists) and the first mountaineers to ascend Alpine summits. Those who visited the Alps in their spare time needed guides and escorts. Being a mountain guide became a new profession, the first profession in tourism, while ingenious inn-keepers became the first hoteliers.

The founding of mountaineering societies and tourist clubs in all the Alpine countries, the first tourist railways into forgotten valleys, rack-railways and cableways reaching into the heart of the high mountains, family hotels and the first thermal spas characterized Alpine tourism at the end of the 19th century and in the years prior to the First World War. An increasing number of people came to the Alps with enough time and money for vacations and recreation.

In the last decades of the 20th century tourism was no longer the privilege of the rich but the everyday need of a hundred million visitors. Unfortunately, today's mass tourism loses the noble content of pioneer times, when it brought social and material progress. The elemental beauties of Alpine nature, which enthused pioneering tourists, are becoming merchandise for self-centred interests outside the Alps. Will these mountains, thanks to land speculators, become virtual stage scenery like artificial ski-slopes and artificial mountains kept under glass in Dubai?

After forty years of constant development, winter tourism experienced a panic-stricken sobering up on account of climate change. Winters with less and less snow are more and more frequent, but there seems no end to wasteful bad habits. Who pays for the electricity for snow cannon, for the night-time illumination of ski-slopes, for the water used to make artificial snow? Whose bill is it when late in the evening some ski snobs swirl down exaggeratedly bright ski routes? A super tourist attraction or simply abuse? And ignorance of the fact that nature and people need darkness, peace and rest at night.

For those responsible for winter tourism a time of new innovations and ingenuity is coming. The Alps will always be a popular destination. With snow or without it.

EVALUATING THE ALPS, PROTECTION AND PRESERVATION - A VISION OF THE FUTURE

We have only one set of the Alps! A sensitive ecosystem on which our life depends. Water, air, earth and its fruits, forests, unending opportunities for spiritual enrichment and physical relaxation. There is a Latin proverb: *variatio delectat*, change is a delight. The biotic, landscape, cultural and linguistic diversity constitutes the immeasurable wealth of the Alps. Sometimes it seems as if certain people are obsessed with preventing that diversity.

We deal with the Alps as with our own stomach. We squash all manner of things into it, although knowing that it is not right, that it is detrimental to our health, that it is too much. For decades it patiently puts up with our harmful greed, until it begins to rebel. If we do not pay attention to the reactions, it starts to deteriorate beyond repair. Isn't it like that with the Alps as well? The yearly more frequent floods, destruction from raging torrents, landslides and rockfall, the derisively ever decreasing quantities of snow for winter tourism, and global warming can be seen as warning reactions, showing that something is wrong in our attitude to the Alps.

There is evidence of human existence in the Alps for at least 5500 years, and with intervals for 10,000 years. People survived all the ruthless trials of natural catastrophes and climatic changes, of famine, poverty and exodus. Perhaps because they knew how to live differently, to believe and trust in something we no longer know and which, on the symbolic level, is preserved in the cultural tradition, in myths and legends. The 3000-year-old art messages, engraved in rocks, we still cannot elucidate. No-one knows what the coded inscription on Ötzi's mummified skin means.

The Alps as the birds see them are becoming increasingly a world of memories, of changed images and disturbing content, which we do not want to see and acknowledge. The birds cannot see the differences between the present state of affairs and that of 50 years ago. Timelessly, yet every year anew, they fly continuously over the Alps, calm us with their song, build nests, are at home here, depart and return once more. We do not know if perhaps instinctively they already sense the coming changes.

The view from the air is the view from a distance. It is not given to everyone to fly around like birds above the mountains. But we have the opportunity and good fortune to live in the Alps; and the responsibility to see that all other forms of life live with us too.

I do not believe the pessimistic predictions that people will be the last living creatures on Earth, who as punishment for their violence against nature will have to witness the apocalyptic end of the world. I am convinced that at the beginning of the third millenium, we have every possibility to revive and experience a time of new challenges and a new creative revolution in the sense of the neolithic regeneration. We also have every possibility not to experience this. If we do not want to do what we ought to and what we could do. The indications are simple and clear for everybody: the drying up of springs and the contamination of drinking water with our effluents, the dying of the forests and of the bees, the clearance sale of the beauties of Alpine valleys, which have no price but only endless value, the wanton construction on land not intended for building, and the crazy trading with Alpine land, the legacy of our ancestors, which is not just a heap of worthless brown soil, but the sediment of a spiritual tradition, of millenia of adapting, believing, feeling emotion and surviving.

Tectonic movements are needed in our heads and our way of thinking. If they do not take place, we will experience even greater tectonic and climactic shifts in our natural environment.

This wonderful world called the Alps was not created as a testing ground for leisure-time follies and competitiveness nor as a laboratory for altering places and scoffing at the sensitive natural balance.

There is nobody who would dare to claim in public that he is against the protection and preservation of the Alps. All are for this. But only as far as the borders of their own egocentric interests. The area of lies, extortion and arrogant self-interest begins on this invisible line. The biggest exploiters and destroyers of Alpine nature cynically present themselves as the greatest guardians of this nature and immediately mock every objection to their ruthlessness as setting up obstacles to progress. Such a confusion of values is not the first example in human history. Legends and folk tales from the distant history of the Alps carry unwritten information. The contents are similar in all the Alpine languages and represent the common memory of the first inhabitants of the Alps. They hide a simple message about the interdependence of all that is living, about the natural order and the limits of what is permitted. It was always wrong when human beings in their presumption overstepped these boundaries. In fact, the preservation of the Alps begins and ends with acknowledging and respecting them.

The view from the air can perhaps give back confidence in the well-tried elements of the 5000-year-old art of survival.

The Drac valley [FRANCE]   N 44° 39' 12" E 06° 15' 31"   ⟳ 3957 m

THE SOUTHERN ALPS

The Cottian Alps [ITALY]

N 44° 24' 31" E 07° 12' 47"   ☊ 3293 m

Plateau de Valensole [FRANCE]

N 43° 51' 19" E 06° 08' 28" ↻ 1107 m

Pic de Bure, 2709 m [FRANCE]

N 44° 36' 13" E 05° 54' 23"   ⦿ 2714 m

Les Penitentes des Mees [FRANCE]

N 44° 02' 11" E 05° 59' 27" ↻ 719 m

The Écrins massif [FRANCE]

N 44° 35' 21" E 06° 07' 33" ⟳ 3469 m

Sisteron, 485 m [FRANCE]

N 44° 11' 36" E 05° 56' 39" Ω 949 m

The Toraggio group [FRANCE / ITALY]

N 44° 00' 37" E 07° 34' 28"   ⟳ 2403 m

La Meije, 3982 m [FRANCE]

N 45° 02' 26" E 06° 10' 13"   ☊ 3338 m

Borgata Caricatori, Comune di Macra [ITALY]

N 44° 29' 32" E 07° 16' 52" ⏾ 1272 m

Vercors [FRANCE]

N 44° 56' 27" E 05° 34' 59"   ⟳ 2078 m

Piedmont vineyards [ITALY]

N 44° 37' 07" E 07° 59' 29" ☉ 741 m

Montagne de Saint-Genis [FRANCE]

N 44° 22' 59" E 05° 52' 40"   ⟳ 1765 m

Saint-Auban-d'Oze, 943 m [FRANCE]

N 44° 28' 43" E 05° 49' 30" ⌖ 1497 m

The Mont Aiguille, 2086 m [FRANCE]

N 44° 52' 13" E 05° 36' 49"   ⟳ 1985 m

L'Authion, 2010 m [FRANCE]

N 43° 58' 50" E 07° 25' 55" ☉ 2589 m

Le Monêtier-Les-Bains, 1487 m [FRANCE]

N 44° 57' 45" E 06° 27' 49"   ↻ 4078 m

Le Parc Naturel Régional du Queyras [FRANCE]

N 44° 45' 13" E 06° 51' 30"   ⊘ 3949 m

Apricale, 250 m [ITALY]

N 43° 52' 09" E 07° 38' 48" ⟳ 1103 m

Montagne de Faraut, 2493 m [FRANCE]

N 44° 38' 14" E 06° 15' 59" ⟳ 4010 m

Monaco [MONACO]

The D'Arsine glacial lakes, 2450 m [FRANCE]

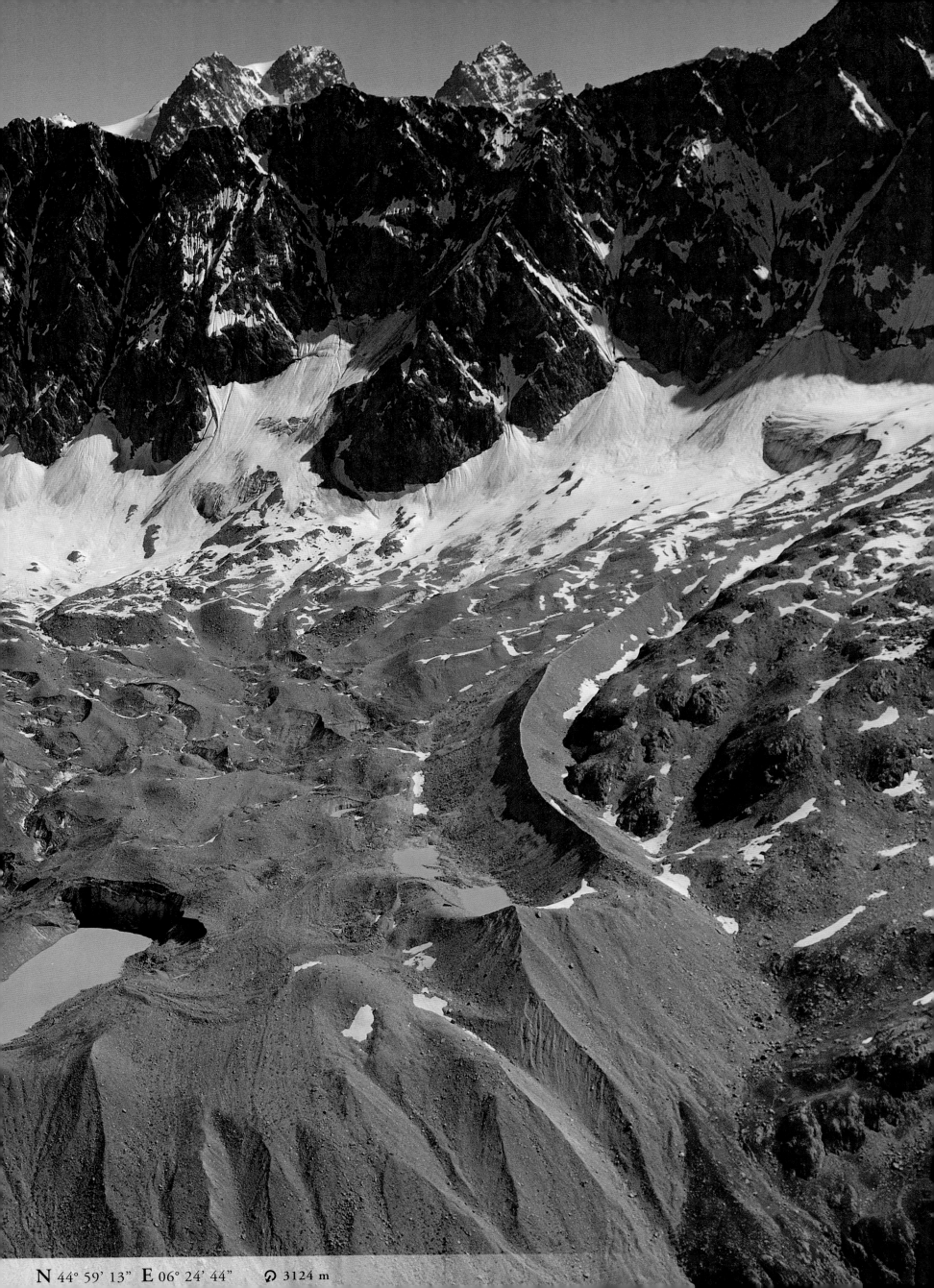

N 44° 59' 13" E 06° 24' 44"   3124 m

Col de Tende [FRANCE / ITALY]

N 44° 08' 03" E 07° 34' 43"   ⟳ 2502 m

Montagne des Agneaux [FRANCE]

N 44° 57' 10" E 06° 27' 02"   ⌖ 4329 m

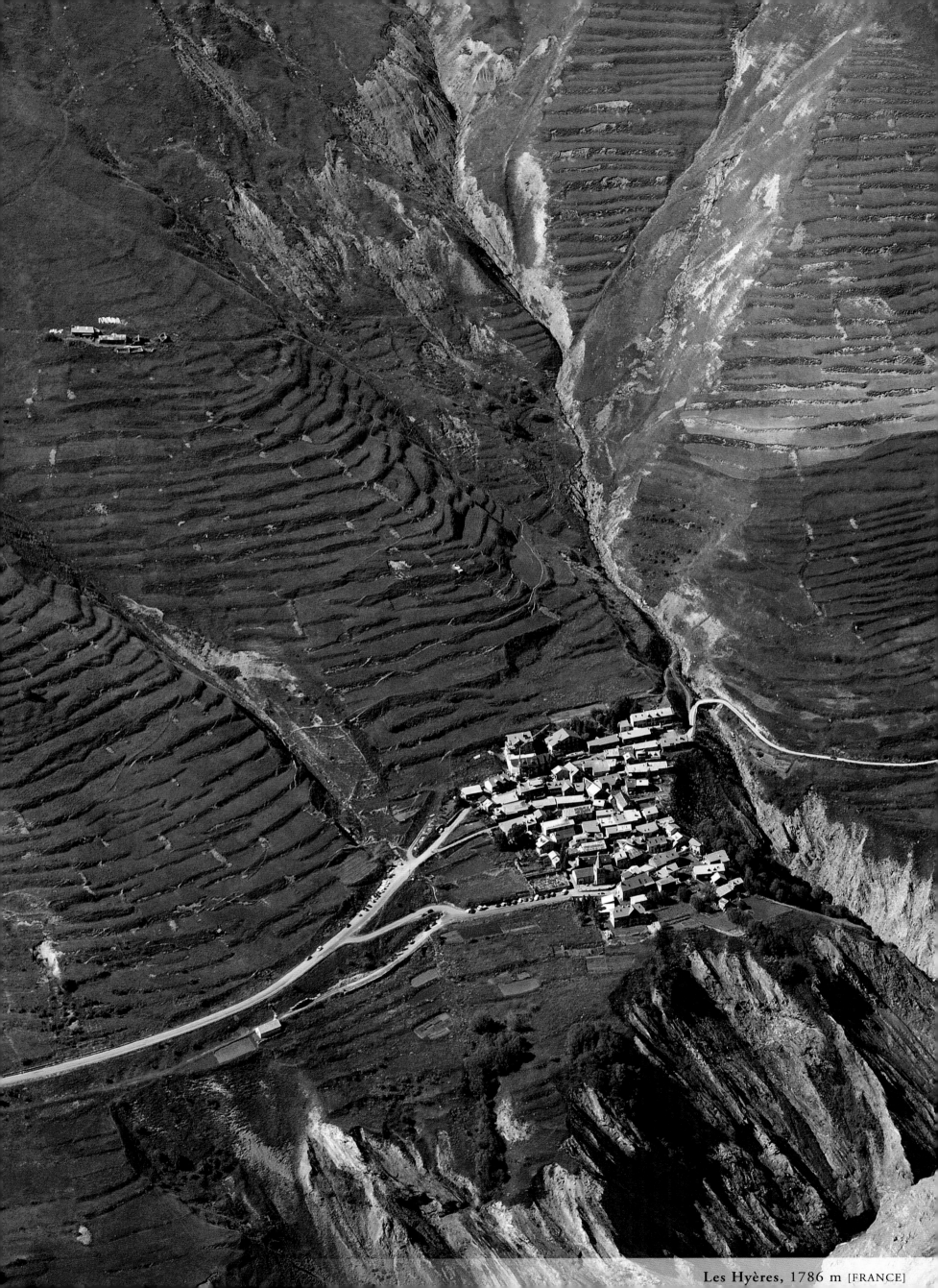

Les Hyères, 1786 m [FRANCE]

N 45° 02' 13" E 06° 19' 03"   ☊ 3092 m

Le Sirac, 3440 m [FRANCE]

N 44° 45' 47" E 06° 25' 07"   ♎ 4023 m

Faye - Ventavon [FRANCE]

N 44° 10' 14" E 05° 59' 53"   ⌀ 1325 m

Monte Viso / *Monviso*, 3841 m [ITALY]

N 44° 38' 31" E 07° 03' 39"   ⏎ 4038 m

Moustiers Sainte-Marie, 630 m [FRANCE]

N 43° 50' 28" E 06° 12' 25"   1249 m

Les Aiguilles d'Arves, 3514 m [FRANCE]

N 44° 59' 34" E 06° 22' 16" ☊ 4211 m

Col de Tende, 1870 m [ITALY / FRANCE]

N 44° 09' 14" E 07° 33' 24"   ⦾ 2472 m

Les Écrins National Park [FRANCE]

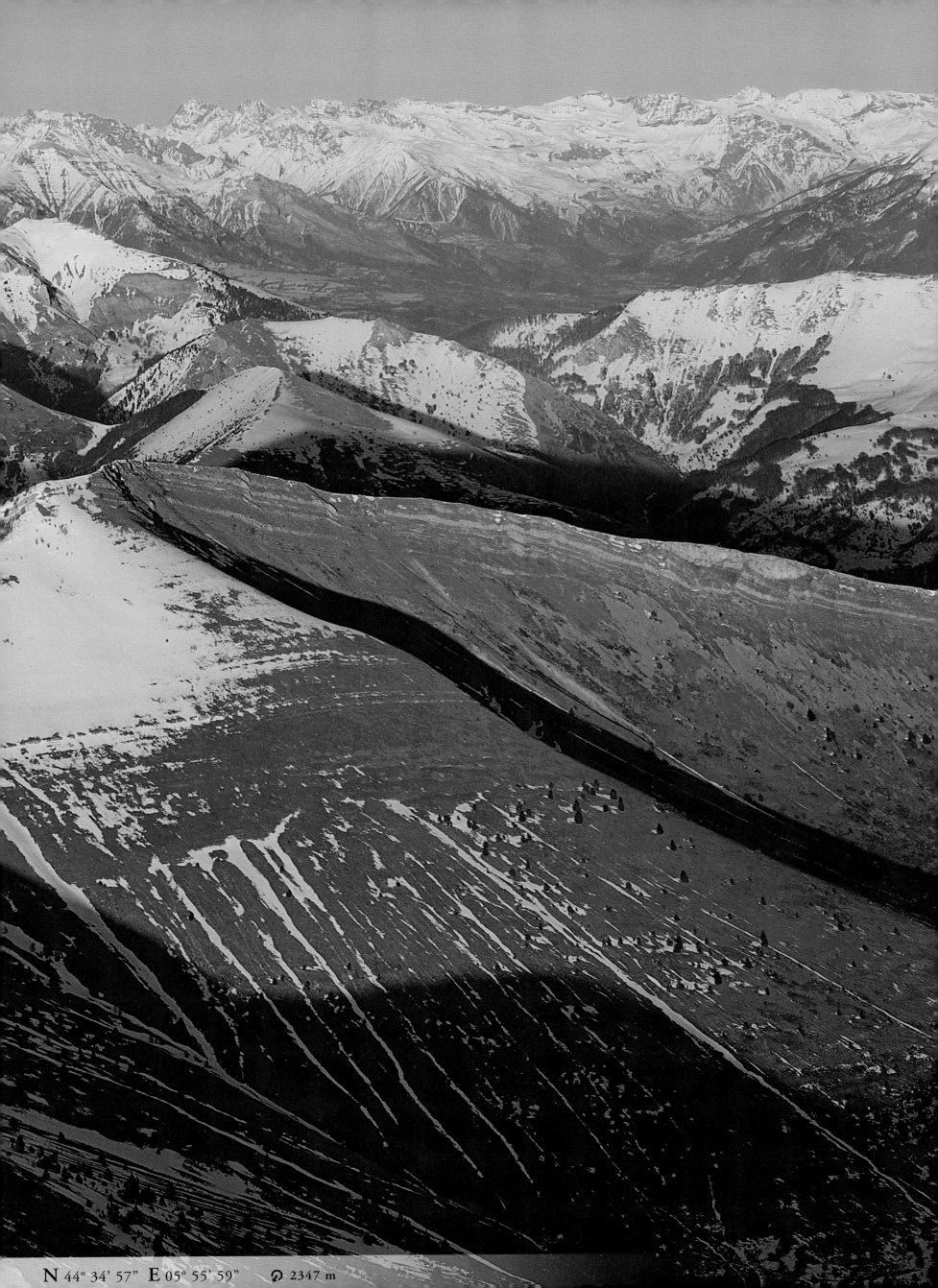

N 44° 34' 57" E 05° 55' 59" ☉ 2347 m

Mont d'Aujour, 1834 m [FRANCE]

N 44° 23' 48" E 05° 48' 29" ⟳ 1599 m

Alpi Marittime [ITALY]

N 44° 12' 28" E 07° 19' 58" ⟳ 3715 m

Dronero, 584 m [ITALY]

N 44° 28' 10" E 07° 21' 37" ⟳ 834 m

Monte Viso / *Monviso*, 3841 m [ITALY]

N 44° 36' 06" E 07° 15' 29"   ☉ 2790 m

The village of Rougon in Verdon, 960 m [FRANCE]

N 43° 48' 06" E 06° 23' 38"   1315 m

Veynes [FRANCE]

N 44° 31' 47" E 05° 50' 07"   Ω 1288 m

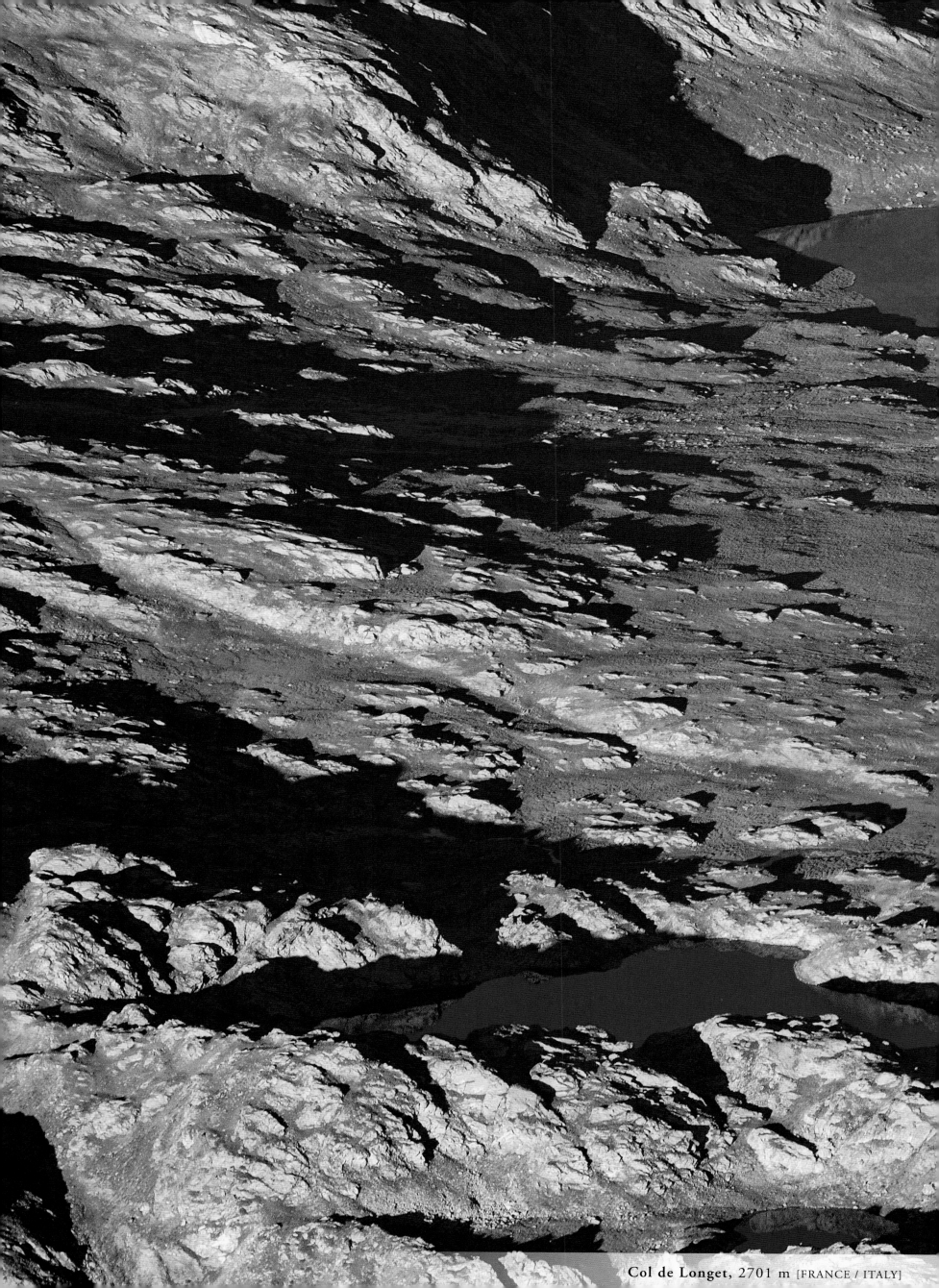

Col de Longet, 2701 m [FRANCE / ITALY]

N 44° 39' 38" E 07° 00' 34"   ♌ 4128 m

Roche de la Muzelle, 3465 m (FRANCE)

N 44° 58' 35" E 06° 06' 01"   ☉ 3562 m

Vallée de la Durance [FRANCE]

N 44° 20' 36" E 05° 53' 52"   ⟳ 1230 m

Punta dell'Argentera, 3297 m [ITALY]

N 44° 12' 34" E 07° 17' 15" ⏦ 3544 m

Diano d'Alba [ITALY]

N 44° 38' 25" E 08° 02' 40" ⟳ 754 m

Barre des Écrins, 4102 m [FRANCE]

N 44° 59' 11" E 06° 24' 42" Ø 4105 m

Chamechaude, 2082 m [FRANCE]

N 45° 14' 05" E 05° 44' 09"   ↻ 1275 m

La Grande Ruine [FRANCE]

N 44° 57' 05" E 06° 23' 22"   ☊ 4342 m

The Briancon mountains [FRANCE]

N 45° 04' 22" E 06° 23' 27" ☉ 4051 m

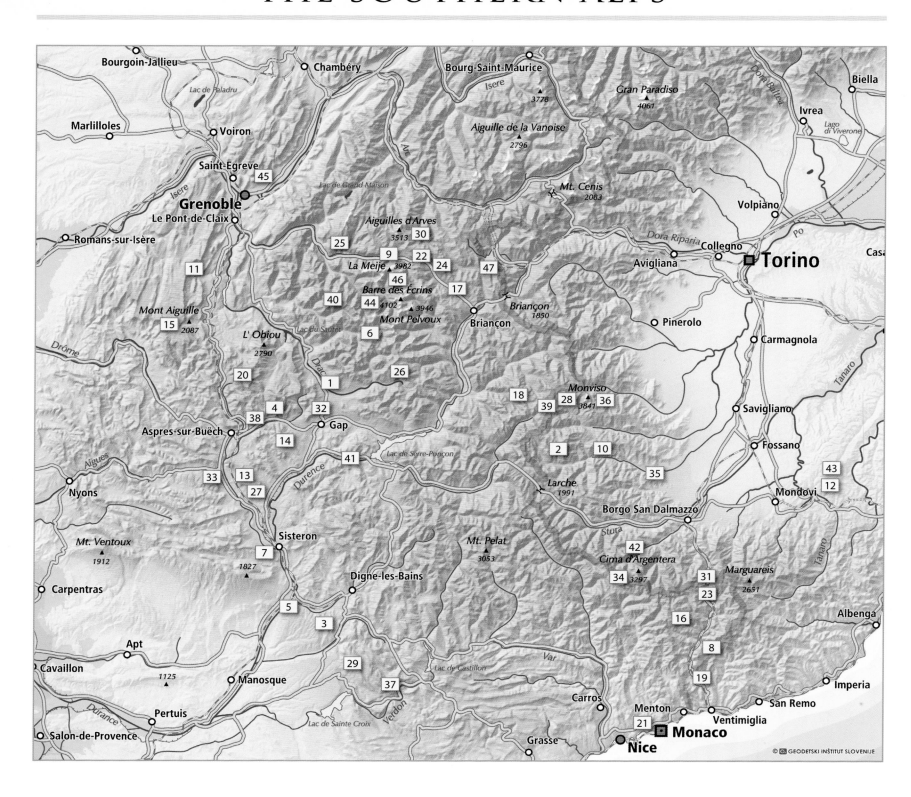

(Map of the Southern Alps with numbered location markers, towns, rivers, and peaks including Grenoble, Torino, Briançon, Monaco, Nice, Gran Paradiso 4061, Barre des Écrins 4102, Mont Pelvoux 3946, La Meije 3982, Monviso 3841, Mt. Ventoux 1912, and others.)

© GEODETSKI INŠTITUT SLOVENIJE

1

Towards the south-west the Champsaur massif drops towards the River Drac, which created a valley separating it from the Dévoluy massif. On the western margin lies one of the bigger towns, Gap, where the administration of the Écrins National Park is also situated. The Drac is dammed to create some artificial lakes and then 130 km further on, near Grenoble, it flows into the River Isère.

THE DRAC VALLEY

2

In the soft light of evening these Alps acquire quite a different appearance from their hard, barren, brown image by day. This massif on the French-Italian border is divided by the Maddalena pass from the Maritime Alps, by the Mont Cenis pass from the Graian Alps, and by the Galibier saddle from the Dauphiné. The headwaters of the big rivers Durance and Po arise in this massif.

THE COTTIAN ALPS

3

In the extreme south-west of the Alpine chain lie the Provençal Alps - Alpes de Haute Provence - which descend from an altitude of 3000 m to the Durance valley. The lowest slopes, where the Valensole plateau is situated, near Puimoisson, are intensively farmed. Broad fields of lavender stretch on both sides of the small River Colostre.

PLATEAU DE VALENSOLE

4

This peak represents the southern part of the Dévoluy massif. An astronomical observatory stands on its summit. The sheer south-west face plunges into the Buëch valley, while the northern slopes provide extensive skiing above the tourist town of Agnières, above the Festre pass.

PIC DE BURE, 2709 m

LES PENITENTES DES MEES

On the northern end of the Valensole plateau stands a chain of 100-metre-high towers above the ancient village of Les Mees (well-known for its olive oil), at the confluence of the Bléone and Durance. An old legend relates that the towers are actually monks from the mountain Lure, whom the hermit St Donatus changed to stone because they were flirting with beautiful Moorish women.

SISTERON

The historical town of Sisteron, the jewel of Provence, lies strategically where the Durance battles through the compressed strata of the Baume and Moulard mountain ridges. Above the old town core stands a fortification over 800 years old. Sisteron was settled 4000 years ago. The Romans left their traces here, as did Napoleon and WW2, with the bridge and town core destroyed.

LA MEIJE, 3982 m

In the Écrins massif La Meije is the dominant summit above the Romanche valley, into which many glaciers descend from the north faces. From the ski resort of La Grave (1417 m) gondolas take visitors to the top of the Girose Glacier at an altitude of 3512 m. Skiing is possible here even in the warmest part of the year.

VERCORS

The Vercors range displays sheer, 300-metre-high east faces, while to the west, forested slopes drop gently to a plateau. During WW2, a rural French resistance movement formed here, climaxing in the foundation of the Vercors Republic, the first liberated French territory after the German occupation. One of the best-known Stone Age sites in the French Alps lies on these plateaus.

MONTAGNE DE SAINT-GENIS

This mountain, which on a satellite photo looks like a giant crater, was named after the settlement at its western foot. Saint Genis lies in a triangle before the confluence of the Buëch and Durance rivers in the Provençal Alps. The height of its limestone rim varies from 700 to 1432 m.

MONT AIGUILLE, 2086 m

Mont Aiguille rises in the Vercors Regional Nature Park, in the south-eastern part of this massif. Its isolated position and perpendicular faces on all sides made it one of the seven wonders of the Dauphiné. Despite its demanding nature, the peak was first ascended as early as 1492.

LE MONÊTIER-LES-BAINS

This settlement lies in the Guisane valley between the Lautaret pass and Briançon, the highest town in the Alps. The western slopes ascend to the three-thousanders Pic de Clouzis, Pointe des Arcas and Pic de Dormillouse, while the eastern slopes climb to the Noire ridge.

APRICALE

The medieval village of Apricale, one of the most beautiful villages in Italy, is located on the southern slopes of the Ligurian Alps, only 13 km from the sea. Its houses are strung like a compact bunch of grapes along a ridge between steep ravines above the Côte d'Azur, near San Remo. This region was settled in prehistoric times, while the village was established in the 10th century.

THE ÉCRINS MASSIF

The mightiest massif in the Southern Alps comprises Pelvoux and Champsaur. Virtually the entire region has been protected since 1973 as a national park - Parc National des Écrins. The southern silhouette is created by the practically 4000-metre-high peaks of L'Ailefroide (3927 m), Pic Sans Nom (3913 m) and Mont Pelvoux (3932 m).

THE TORAGGIO GROUP – THE LIGURIAN ALPS

The roughly 2000-metre-high summits of the Toraggio group on the border between France and Italy are only a good 20 km from the Gulf of Liguria as the crow flies. Despite their altitude, the Mediterranean influence is seen in that the southern slopes are covered with vegetation to the very top.

BORGATA CARICATORI, COMUNE DI MACRA

Formerly there were old traffic routes through the Maira valley, where stone-built medieval villages still stand today. Etruscans, Occitans and Romans left their traces here. Occitan (langue d'oc) is the oldest Romance language, which has been preserved in this valley until now. Many Occitan paths have been made along the valley and river banks to revive the ancient tradition.

PIEDMONT VINEYARDS

The hilly Langhe region lies at the foot of the Ligurian Alps, yet is only a few dozen kilometres away from the Mediterranean coast. The Celts, who settled here 3500 years ago, produced wine even then. Today the region is famous for its extensive vineyards, orchards and truffles.

SAINT-AUBAN-D'OZ

Just a few kilometres west of the semi-circular peak of Ceuse with its necklace of limestone faces, which provide a mecca for free climbing, lies a geomorphically varied and agriculturally fertile valley around the small village of Saint-Auban-d'Oze. The rocky summit of Pic de Bure in the Dévoluy massif can be seen in the background.

L'AUTHION

The L'Authion mountain range lies in the Mercantour National Park, which comprises part of the Maritime Alps and the Provençal Alps. Many military engagements took place here in the past, as evidenced today by fortifications and bunkers.

LE PARC NATUREL RÉGIONAL DU QUEYRAS

This regional park was founded in 1977 in the south-western, French part of the Cottian Alps. It covers an area of 66,000 hectares between Briançon and the Italian border. The highest summit in the park is Font Sancte (3385 m). Due to the Mediterranean influence, the mountains exhibit diverse flora growing to a high altitude.

MONTAGNE DE FARAUT, 2493 m

On the south-western threshold of the Écrins massif stands the Dévoluy range, which is divided in a north-south direction by the valley with the Festre saddle, where there are some well-known ski centres on the northern slopes of Pic de Bure.

MONACO

The principality of Monaco is the second smallest state in the world and has the greatest population density. It lies on the Côte d'Azur, where the terrain rises steeply to the Maritime Alps. It is here that the Alps either begin or end. The influence of the sea in the Gulf of Liguria is felt right up to the loftiest summits, over 3000 metres high.

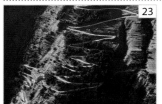

COL DE TENDE

Despite the road and railway which disappear in the tunnel under the Tende pass, the wonderfully panoramic road over the pass is much used today by mountain bikers, motorcyclists and paragliders. The road is said to have been built by the Phoenicians on their merchant travels, and was also used by the Greeks and Romans.

LES HYÈRES

On the right bank of the Maurian stream, which flows from the glacial Lac du Goléon, lies the small, idyllic village of Les Hyères, a little before La Grave. It is surrounded by numerous terraces, which give a characteristic appearance to the valley of the River Romanche, below the glacier-covered north faces of La Meije.

FAYE - VENTAVON

Between these two small villages there is an eroded plateau, where the natural elements have carved out many ravines and gorges. The landscape is more reminiscent of the semi-desert regions of the American West than of the gentle Provençal farmlands rich with lavender.

MOUSTIERS-STE-MARIE

This ancient village lies some kilometres north of Lake Ste-Croix in the Provençal Alps. It nestles below steep cliffs which are linked high above the village by a 227-m-long iron chain across the gorge with a red star in the middle. Moustiers is famous for its traditional pottery. In the village centre stands the renovated 12th-century church of Notre Dame.

COL DE TENDE, 1870 m

The Tende high-altitude pass on the border between France and Italy divides the two massifs of the Maritime and Ligurian Alps. A tunnel was built under the pass as early as 1898. The central fortification on the pass bears witness to the numerous battles between the French and Italians for dominance over the territory and access to the sea.

MONT D' AUJOUR, 1834 m

This ridge of broken limestones extends in an east-west direction between the Buëch and Durance valleys, in the vicinity of Savounon, which is situated on an ancient Roman road. The region is noted for its sheep-breeding.

DRONERO

Dronero is situated at the mouth of the Maira valley, near Cuneo in Piedmont. The River Maira, which flows into the River Po, has its headwaters below the Maddalena saddle on the border between the Maritime and the Cottian Alps. The old core of the town is linked with the newer part on the left bank of the Maira by a bridge that is practically 600 years old.

THE D'ARSINE GLACIAL LAKES, 2450 m

The Dauphiné mountain massif ends in the north-east with the vertical faces of Les Agneaux and Pic de Neige Cordier, below which lies the Glacier d'Arsine with its wonderful glacial lakes in the terminal moraine. Their waters flow into the valley of the River Guisane at the eastern margin of the Écrins National Park.

MONTAGNE DES AGNEAUX

In this mountain group, the Pyramide and Tuckett Glaciers reach right to the summit. Westwards there is a steep drop from the high peaks into the valley of the Blanc glacier, which winds towards the summit of Barre des Écrins. In the background are three-thousanders in the Pelvoux group, extending from Mont Pelvoux via Pic Sans Nom to L'Ailefroide.

LE SIRAC, 3440 m

From the central Pelvoux massif in the Dauphiné, the ridges gradually lose height across Les Bans (3669 m), Pic de Bonvoisin (3560 m), as far as Le Sirac, which is the last high sentinel in the southern part of the Les Écrins National Park. In the background is the long Vercors mountain chain.

MONTE VISO / MONVISO, 3841 m

This pyramidal mountain rises in the Cottian Alps. Its western ridges continue towards the French Dauphiné and to the south towards the chain of the Maritime Alps. The area around Monte Viso was settled in prehistoric times, as is proved by the Neolithic archaeological finds.

LES AIGUILLES D'ARVES 3514 m

In the Grandes Rousses massif, which lies north of the Romanche valley, west of the Col du Galibier saddle and east of the high-altitude ski resort Alpe d'Huez, the most easily recognized mountains are the three pyramidal peaks known as the Aiguilles d'Arves.

LES ÉCRINS NATIONAL PARK

This national park covers over 270,000 hectares and ranges from 800 to 4102 m in altitude. Of this area, only 3000 ha are forested, while glaciers occupy 17,000 ha, but they are rapidly disappearing. About 600,000 hikers, alpinists and tourists visit the park annually. Of the 1800 plant species, as many as 35 are endemic.

ALPI MARITTIME

The three-thousanders of the Maritime Alps are situated in the Italian nature park of the same name and the French Mercantour National Park. They are only 50 km away from the Gulf of Liguria, a position providing fairly mild climatic conditions.

MONTE VISO / MONVISO, 3841 m

This impressive mountain surpasses the surrounding summits by at least 500 m. Its characteristic shape is visible from many kilometres away. The eastern slopes, cleft by deep valleys, descend to Piedmont and the Po plain. The main source of the River Po is in the northern massif, near Piano.

ROUGON, VERDON

Verdon is one of the most important testing grounds for free climbing. The sound limestone in steep faces above the gorge of the River Verdon offers a multiplicity of demanding routes. The rock faces above the gorge also form the largest area inhabited by the griffon vulture in the Alps. The small village of Rougon lies on the right bank of the Verdon.

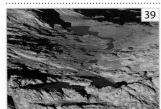

COL DE LONGET, 2701m

The lakes on the Longet saddle straddle the border between France and Italy. Lake Longet is French and lies very close to the Queyras Regional Park. On the Italian side are Lago Blu and Lago Nero, whose surplus water drains into the valley of the River Varaita, a left tributary of the River Po.

VALLÉE DE LA DURANCE

The Durance is one of the main rivers in the French part of the Southern Alps. It rises below the Montgenèvre saddle near Briançon, combines with the Rivers Guisane, Buëch and Verdon, and after 304 km ends its route through Provence by flowing into the Rhône. All the way the Durance is exploited for energy; here before reaching Sisteron, it flows as a monotonous canal.

DIANO D'ALBA

The small village of Diano d'Alba lies in the extreme north-eastern part of the Ligurian Alps on the gentle, vineyard-covered hills of Langhe, in the Cuneo-Piedmont province. The Ligurian, Cottian and Graian Alps form a wonderful backdrop.

CHAMECHAUDE, 2082 m

Chamechaude is the highest peak of the Chartreuse massif, which lines the valley of the River Isère north-east of Grenoble. Here a regional park was created in 1995. It was in these mountains that St Bruno with six adherents founded the strict order of the Carthusians in the monastery La Grande Chartreuse (north of Chamechaude) in 1084.

THE BRIANÇON MOUNTAINS

The Dauphiné ends in the east on the left bank of the River Guisane with the Briançon massif. The easiest route into Italy leads over the Montgenèvre saddle, below which the River Durance has its source. The highest peaks exceed 3000 m.

VEYNES

The fragmented cliffs above Veynes, which lies by the River Buëch, constitute the southernmost slopes of the Dévoluy Massif. Just as on Ceuse, the nearby limestone paradise for free climbing, the rock here is suitable for a range of adrenaline activities. In the background are the Ferrand summits, almost 3000 metres high, above the Festre saddle.

ROCHE DE LA MUZELLE 3465 m

This mountain lies in the Écrins National Park in the Dauphiné. On its northern side the Muzelle Glacier nearly reaches the summit. The glacial waters flow into the valley of the River Vénéon, which is fed by the northern and north-western glaciers of the Pelvoux massif.

PUNTA DELL'ARGENTERA 3297 m

The Maritime Alps Nature Park is the largest park in Piedmont. Some of its summits exceed 3000 m, the highest being Dell'Argentera, and the most southerly Alpine glaciers are situated here. The park, which is connected with the Mercantour National Park in France, has over 80 glacial lakes and rich flora and fauna.

BARRE DES ÉCRINS, 4102 m

This is the most southerly four-thousander in the Alps and also the highest point in the Écrins massif in the Dauphiné (between the Durance in Isère valleys), which is protected as a national park. The mountain is easily identified from the north by the Blanc Glacier, which reaches almost to the summit. In the background is the trapezoidal peak L'Ailefroide (3954 m).

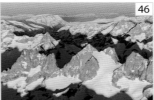

LA GRANDE RUINE

The group of summits known as La Grande Ruine stands between Barre des Écrins and La Meije. Alpinists usually climb to the summit via the Agneaux Glacier and the Planchard mountain refuge. In the background lies the high-altitude ski centre of La Grave La Meije, which is reached by gondolas from the Romanche valley.

The Mont Blanc massif [FRANCE]   N 46° 00' 20" E 06° 45' 37"   ⟳ 4128 m

THE WESTERN ALPS

Mont Blanc, 4807 m [FRANCE]

N 45° 54' 04" E 06° 45' 14" ↻ 5053 m

The Bernese Alps [SWITZERLAND]

N 46° 32' 11" E 08° 26' 05"   ☉ 5179 m

Lake Thun, 557 m [SWITZERLAND]

N 46° 41' 09" E 07° 42' 15"   ↻ 1479 m

The Rhône Glacier [SWITZERLAND]

N 46° 33' 15" E 08° 21' 48" ↻ 3828 m

Mont Trelod, 2181 m [FRANCE]

N 45° 46' 23" E 06° 14' 26"   3116 m

Engstligental [SWITZERLAND]

N 46° 36' 23" E 07° 37' 58" ↻ 2896 m

Monte Rosa - Dofourspitze, 4634 m, Lyskamm, 4527 m [SWITZERLAND]

N 46° 01' 03" E 07° 41' 53" ⏾ 4350 m

Grivola, 3969 m [ITALY]

N 45° 36' 14" E 07° 14' 10"   ↻ 4401 m

The Grandes Jorasses, 4208 m [FRANCE]

N 46° 00' 55" E 06° 44' 22"   ↻ 4211 m

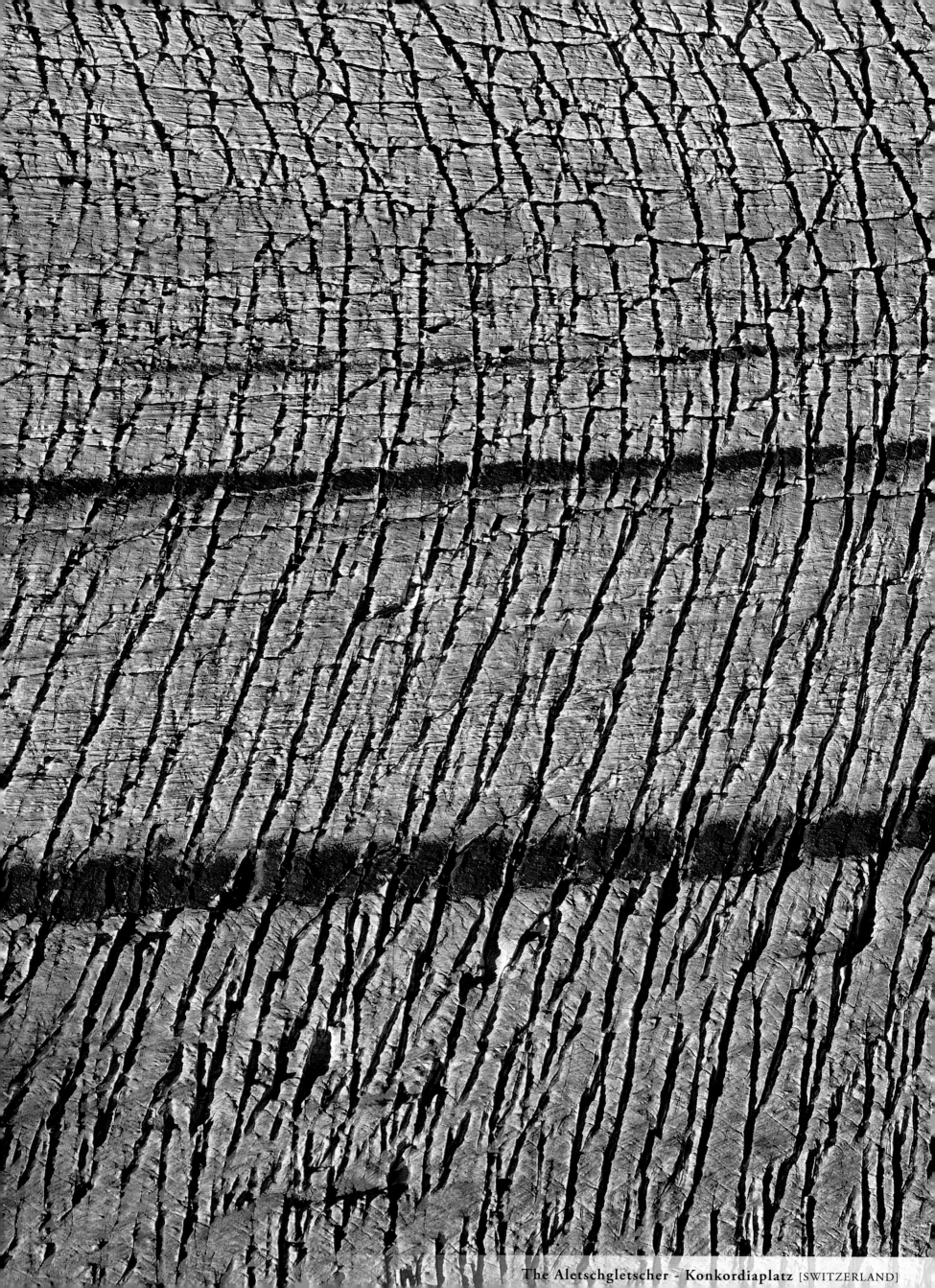

The Aletschgletscher - Konkordiaplatz [SWITZERLAND]

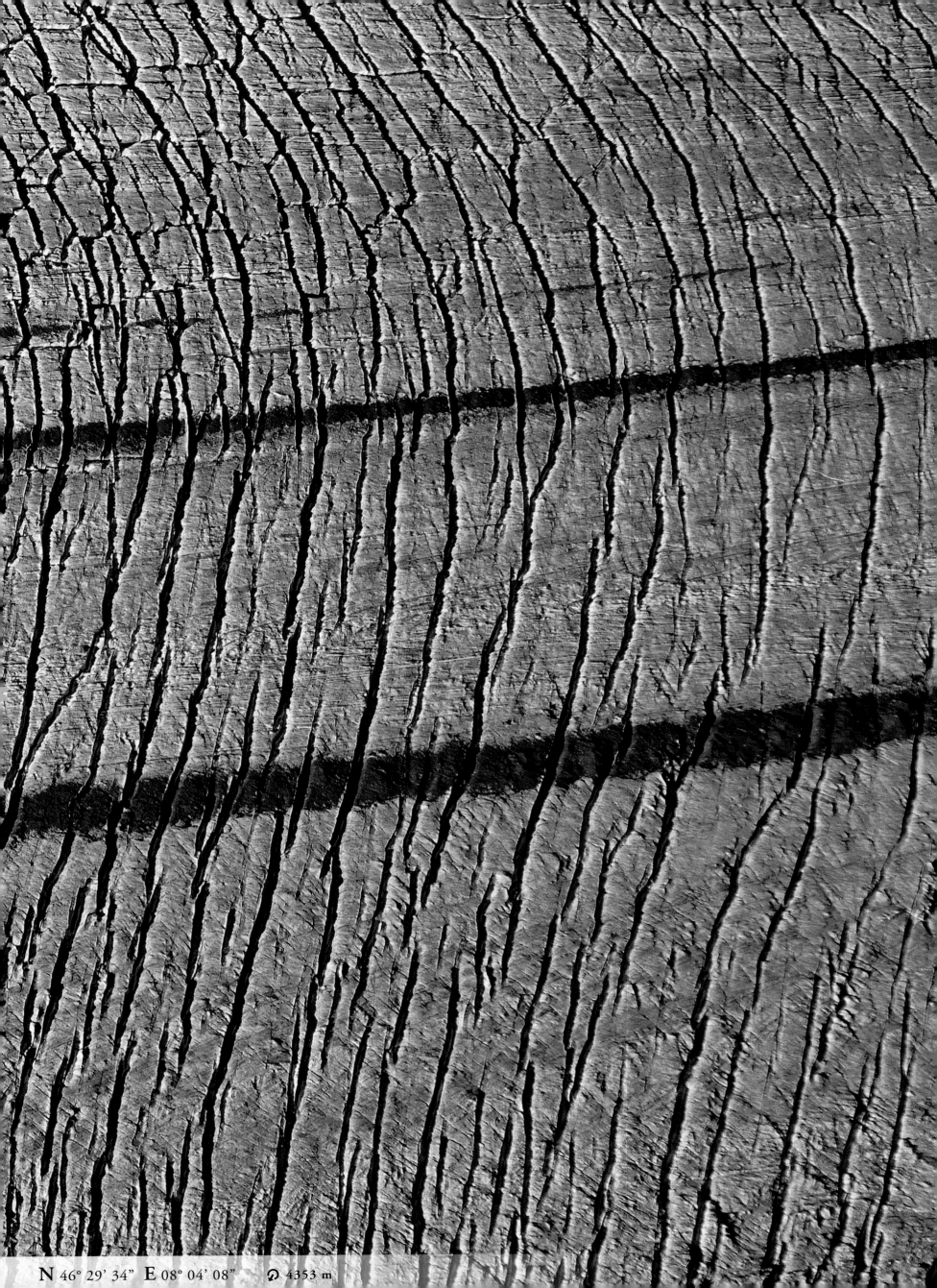

N 46° 29' 34" E 08° 04' 08"   4353 m

The Bernese Alps [SWITZERLAND]

N 46° 32' 17" E 07° 49' 26"   ⟳ 4345 m

The Finsteraarhorn - Schreckhorn massif [SWITZERLAND]

N 46° 35' 01" E 08° 21' 00"   ⟳ 4045 m

The Glarner Alps [SWITZERLAND]

N 47° 04' 06" E 09° 16' 21" Ⓞ 2115 m

Mont Blanc, 4807 m [FRANCE]

N 45° 46' 58" E 06° 45' 44"   ⌀ 4785 m

Dent du Brenleire, 2353 m, Follieran, 2340 m, Vanil Noir, 2389 m [SWITZERLAND]

N 46° 35' 31" E 07° 09' 59" ⌖ 2055 m

The Bernese Oberland [SWITZERLAND]

N 46° 35' 27" E 07° 34' 08" ⟳ 3467 m

Matterhorn / *Cervino* / *Mt. Cervin*, 4478 m [SWITZERLAND]

N 45° 59' 50" E 07° 40' 44"   ☉ 4282 m

The Wilerhorn, 3307 m, The Bietschhorn, 3934 m [SWITZERLAND]

N 46° 19' 32" E 07° 51' 27"   𝒪 4625 m

Gran Paradiso, 4061 m [ITALY]

N 45° 36' 27" E 07° 14' 28" ⟳ 4379 m

Grandes Jorasses, 4208 m, Mont Blanc du Tacul, 4248 m [FRANCE]

N 45° 53' 23" E 06° 44' 28" ⊙ 4982 m

The Breithorn, 3785 m [SWITZERLAND]

N 46° 30' 08" E 07° 45' 00" ⌀ 4344 m

Männlichen, 2343 m [SWITZERLAND]

N 46° 34' 52" E 07° 56' 20" ☉ 4037 m

The Matterhorn / *Cervino* / *Mt. Cervin*, 4478 m - the west face [SWITZERLAND / ITALY]

N 45° 58' 56" E 07° 37' 46"   ⌀ 4315 m

The Eiger, 3970 m, The Mönch, 4107 m [SWITZERLAND]

N 46° 36' 07" E 07° 54' 59" ↻ 3905 m

Dom, 4545 m [SWITZERLAND]

N 46° 10' 12" E 07° 52' 46" ☉ 4202 m

The Dents du Midi, 3257 m [SWITZERLAND]

N 46° 10' 05" E 06° 51' 46" ☉ 3909 m

The Dômes de Miage [FRANCE]

N 45° 50' 15" E 06° 46' 06" ⟳ 4847 m

The Jungfrau, 4158 m [SWITZERLAND]

N 46° 39' 04" E 07° 43' 42" ⊙ 2170 m

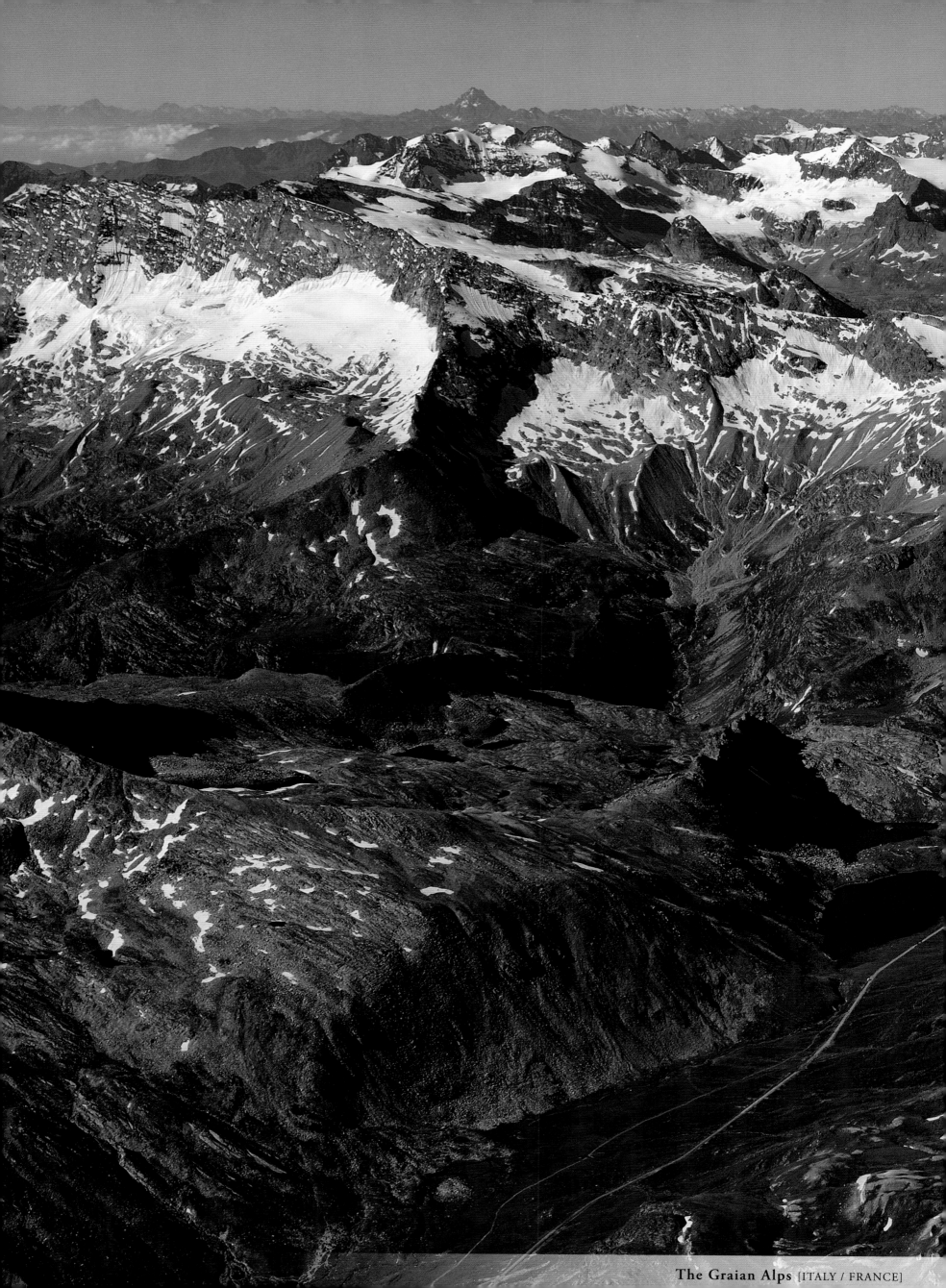

The Graian Alps [ITALY / FRANCE]

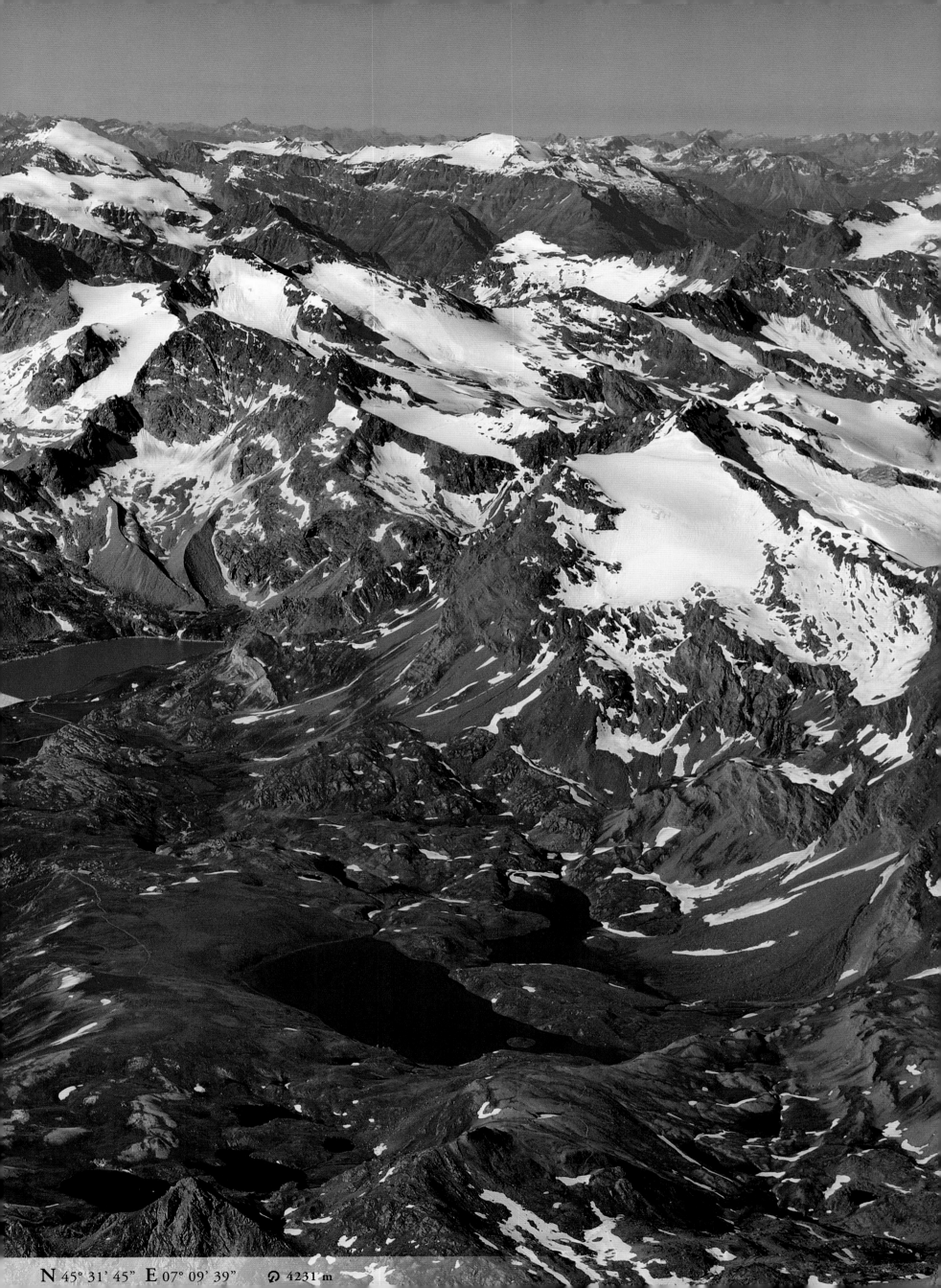

N 45° 31' 45" E 07° 09' 39"   ⌖ 4231 m

Mont Blanc, 4807 m [ITALY]

N 45° 50' 17" E 07° 06' 37"   3860 m

Monte Rosa - Dufourspitze, 4634 m [ITALY / SWITZERLAND]

N 45° 50' 45" E 07° 46' 54" ⟳ 4669 m

Gruyère, 1638 m [SWITZERLAND]

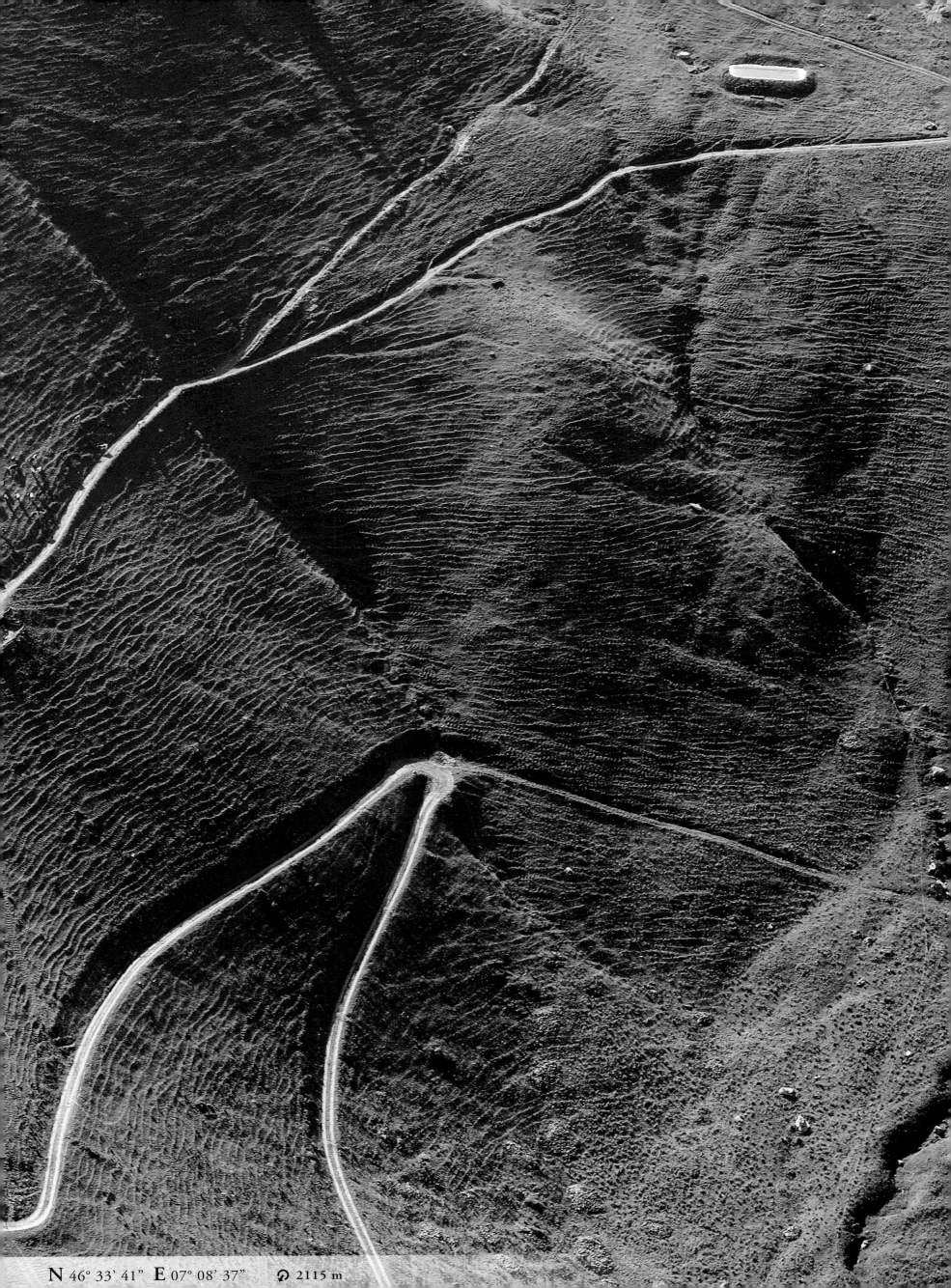

N 46° 33' 41" E 07° 08' 37" ⟳ 2115 m

Cervino / *Matterhorn* / *Mt. Cervin*, 4478 m [ITALY]

N 45° 57' 42" E 07° 42' 29" ⦵ 4220 m

The Bernese and Valais Alps [SWITZERLAND]

N 46° 37' 55" E 08° 15' 53"   ⌀ 3915 m

The Lauteraarhorn, 4042 m [SWITZERLAND]

N 46° 31' 12" E 08° 15' 13"   ⟳ 3985 m

The Kander Glacier, 2800 m [SWITZERLAND]

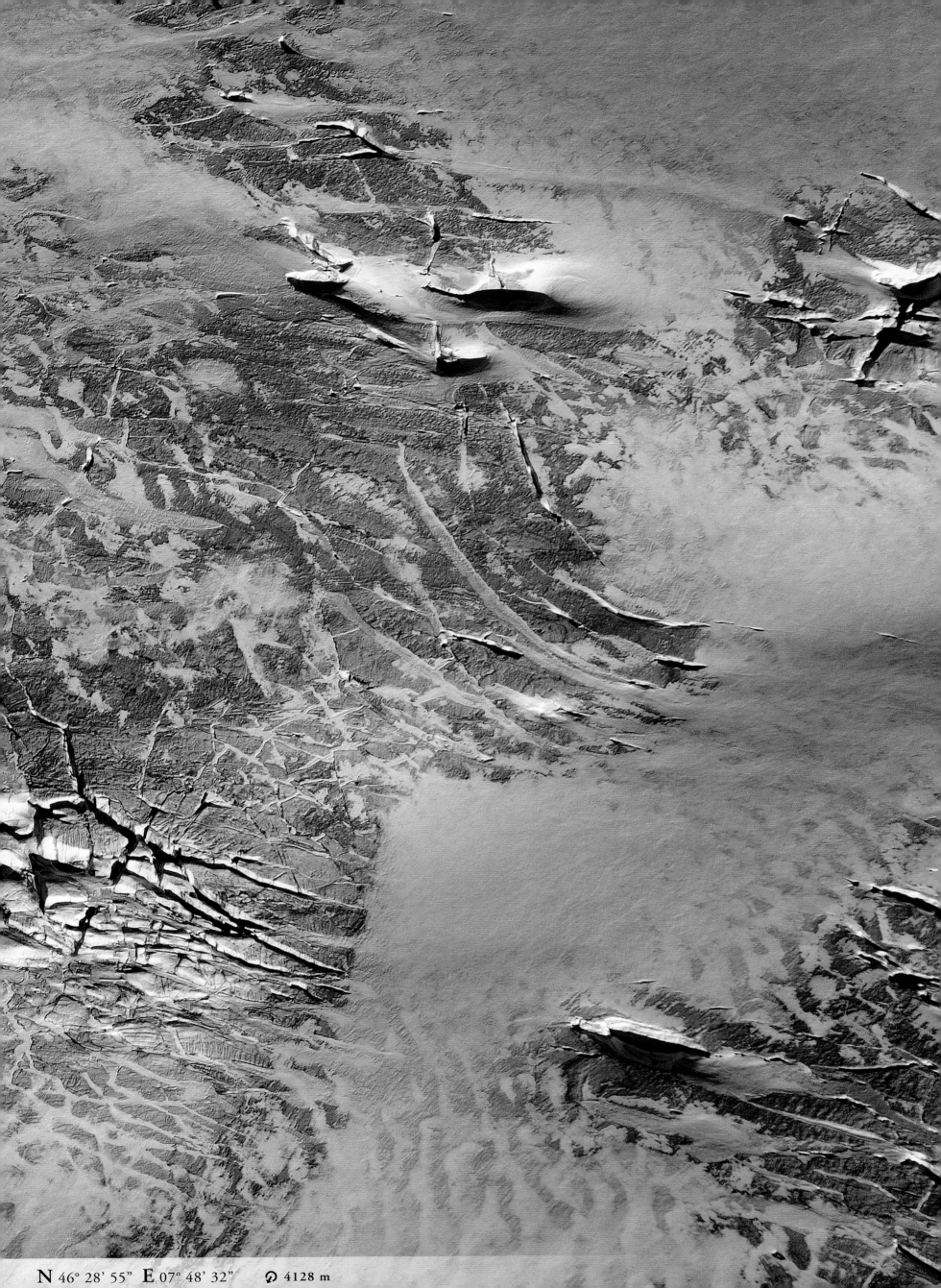

N 46° 28' 55" E 07° 48' 32"   ⟳ 4128 m

The Grand Combin, 4314 m [ITALY / SWITZERLAND]

N 45° 52' 04" E 07° 22' 06" ⌀ 3874 m

The Aletsch Glacier [SWITZERLAND]

N 46° 21' 27" E 08° 05' 02"   ⟳ 5087 m

The Finsteraarhorn, 4274 m [SWITZERLAND]

N 46° 35' 07" E 08° 06' 20" ⌀ 4299 m

The west ridge of the Doldenhorn [SWITZERLAND]

N 46° 28' 26" E 07° 43' 05"   ♋ 4354 m

The Weisshorn, 4505 m [SWITZERLAND]

N 46° 04' 09" E 07° 44' 10"   ⏁ 4312 m

The Bernese Alps [SWITZERLAND]

N 46° 26' 56" E 08° 14' 13"   ↻ 5189 m

The Massif de la Vanoise [FRANCE]

N 45° 17' 21" E 06° 28' 09"   ♂ 3684 m

The Lauterbrunnen face [SWITZERLAND]

N 46° 31' 28" E 07° 52' 59"   ☉ 4119 m

The Massif des Aravis [FRANCE]

N 45° 50' 20" E 06° 33' 14"   ⊘ 4364 m

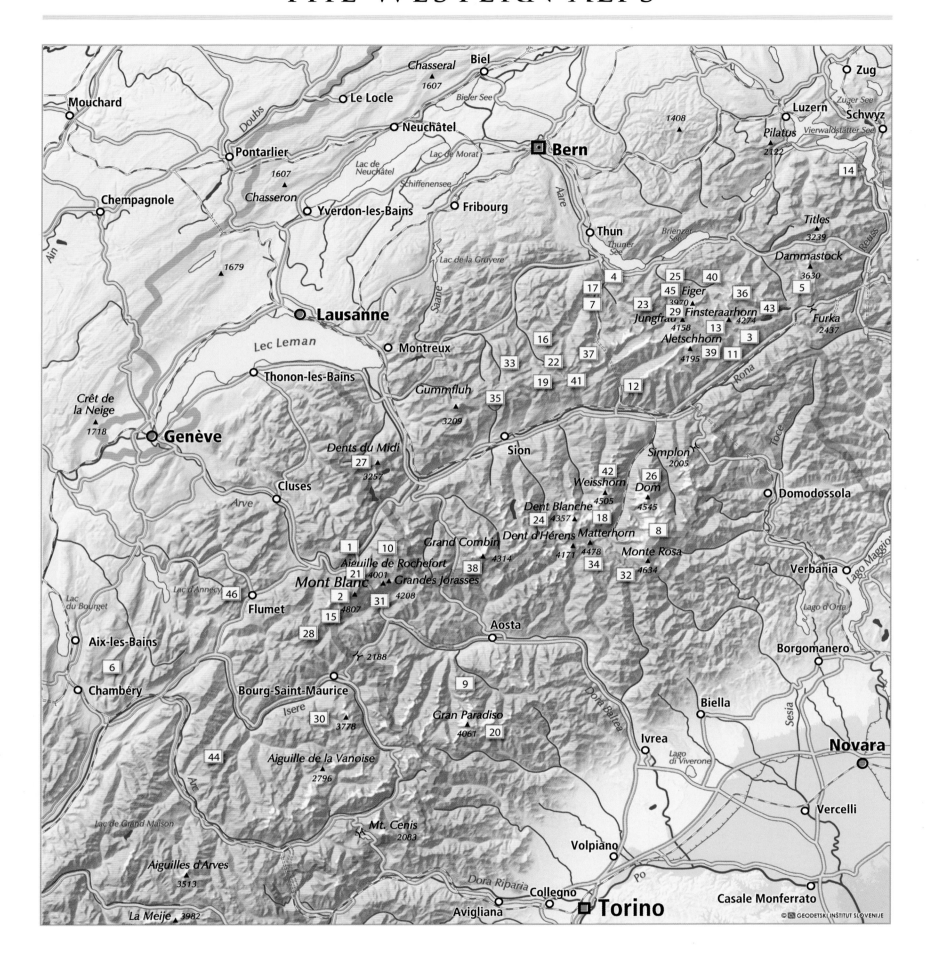

Map labels:

Mouchard · Le Locle · Chasseral · 1607 · Biel · Bieler See · Zug · Luzern · Schwyz · Zuger See · Pilatus 2122 · Vierwaldstätter See · 1408 · Neuchâtel · Bern · Pontarlier · Lac de Neuchâtel · Lac de Morat · Aare · Reuss · Chempagnole · 1607 · Chasseron · Schiffenensee · Fribourg · Titles 3239 · Yverdon-les-Bains · Lac de la Gruyère · Thun · Thuner See · Brienzer See · Dammastock 3630 · 1679 · Saane · 4 · 25 · 40 · 5 · Lausanne · 17 · 45 · Eiger 3970 · 36 · 7 · 23 · Jungfrau · 29 · Finsteraarhorn 4274 · 43 · Furka 2437 · Lec Leman · Montreux · 16 · 4158 · 13 · 3 · Aletschhorn · 39 · 11 · Thonon-les-Bains · 33 · 22 · 37 · 4195 · Crêt de la Neige 1718 · 19 · 41 · 12 · Rona · Gummfluh · 35 · 3209 · Genève · Sion · Simplon 2005 · Toce · Dents du Midi · 27 · 3257 · Weisshorn · 42 · 26 · Dom · Domodossola · Cluses · Arve · Dent Blanche 4505 · 4545 · 24 · 4357 · 18 · 1 · 10 · Grand Combin · Dent d'Hérens · Matterhorn · 8 · Aiguille de Rochefort · 38 · 4314 · 4171 · 4478 · Monte Rosa · Verbania · Lago Maggiore · 21 · 4001 · Grandes Jorasses · 34 · 4634 · Mont Blanc · 2 · 31 · 4208 · 32 · Lago d'Orta · Lac d'Annecy · 46 · Flumet · 15 · 4807 · Aosta · Borgomanero · 28 · 2188 · 9 · Aix-les-Bains · 6 · Biella · Chambéry · Bourg-Saint-Maurice · Isere · Gran Paradiso · Dora Baltea · Ivrea · Novara · 30 · 3778 · 4061 · 20 · Lago di Viverone · 44 · Aiguille de la Vanoise 2796 · Vercelli · Arc · Lac de Grand Maison · Sesia · Mt. Cenis 2083 · Volpiano · Po · Aiguilles d'Arves 3513 · Dora Riparia · Casale Monferrato · La Meije 3982 · Avigliana · Collegno · Torino · © GEODETSKI INŠTITUT SLOVENIJE

THE MONT BLANC MASSIF

1 The chain of peaks in this massif, seen in the light of the setting sun. From the left: Aiguille Verte, with Aiguille du Dru in front, the Mer de Glace valley, the Aiguilles de Chamonix, Aiguille du Midi, Mont Blanc du Tacul, Mont Maudit and the highest summit in Europe, Mont Blanc itself.

MONT BLANC, 4807 m

2 Mont Blanc is the highest mountain in Europe and was first climbed by Paccard and Balmat in 1786. The easiest access routes lead via Aiguille du Midi, Mont Blanc du Tacul and Mont Maudit or via Dôme du Goûter.

THE BERNESE ALPS

The marvellous necklace of the Bernese Alps lies in south-west Switzerland, in the Valais and Bern cantons. The entire chain, occupying a NE-SW direction, is a good 100 km long from Martigny to the Grimsel pass. In the central region its breadth exceeds 30 km.

THE RHÔNE GLACIER

From under the Rhône Glacier, which crawls along the basin of Dammastock (3630 m) in the Urner Alps, flows the River Rhône, which supplies most of the water for Lake Léman. The glacier is melting rapidly and its snout moves constantly higher.

ENGSTLIGENTAL

At the head of the Engstligental valley lies the well-known ski centre of Adelboden. Its eastern slopes descend from the ridge between the summits of Niesen (2362 m) and the Albristhorn (2762 m), while the western slopes rise up to four-thousander peaks.

GRIVOLA, 3969 m

Grivola is the first summit which with its pyramid-like shape rises above the town of Aosta. It stands in the Gran Paradiso National Park between the valleys of Valsavarenche and Val di Cogne. Grivola was first climbed only in 1859, by Tairraz, Ormsby, Bruce, Dayne and Cachat.

THE ALETSCHGLETSCHER – KONKORDIAPLATZ

Konkordiaplatz is the meeting-point of four glaciers, which crawl onwards as the Aletsch Glacier into the Rhône valley. The main sources of this glacier are the Grosser Aletschfirn, the Jungfraufirn, the Ewigschneefeld and the Grueneggfirn.

THE FINSTERAARHORN – SCHRECKHORN MASSIF

Above the Grimsel pass the view opens up into the heart of glacier-encircled mountains. In the foreground is Bächlistock (3247 m), whose slopes descend to the valley of the Aar Glacier. Above it soars the Finsteraarhorn (4274 m), and then its northern neighbours the Lauteraarhorn (4042 m) and the Schreckhorn (4078 m). On the horizon is the snow-clad pyramid of the Fiescherhorn (4049 m).

MONT BLANC, 4807 m

On the southern side the necklace of Mont Blanc summits is formed by the Dômes de Miage and Aiguille de Bionnassay, whose ridge leads right up to the lower summit of Mont Blanc, Dôme du Goûter. The great South Face of the highest peak with the Frêney pillars and the eastern Peuterey ridge is shown here.

THE BERNESE OBERLAND

The grassy ridge between Niesen (2362 m), a tourist viewpoint reached by a mountain railway, and the Albristhorn is simply an extensive pasture above the valley which leads to Adelboden and Kandersteg. Towards the north-east the ridges rise gradually as far as the four-thousanders of the Bernese Alps from the Eiger to the Bietschhorn.

LAKE THUN, 557 m

Beneath the impressive, sheer faces of the Bernese Alps, with their hanging glaciers, lies Lake Thun, covering 2500 km², which is named after the town at its northernmost point. The lake is fed by Lake Brienz, which lies only 6 m higher, and by glacial torrents. On its southern shore is the town of Spiez and behind it the mountains of the Bernese Oberland.

MONT TRELOD, 2181 m

The Bauges range, lying between the towns of Chambery, Annecy and Albertville, is protected as the Bauges Regional Nature Park. As well as its variety of fauna and flora, the park is endowed with extensive pastures, forests and mountains over 2000 metres high.

MONTE ROSA

From the north-west the Monte Rosa massif looks down on the second biggest glacial system in the Alps, the Gornergrat. This 14-km-long mass of ice is fed by the snowfields and northern faces of Monte Rosa, Lyskamm and the Breithorn.

THE GRANDES JORASSES, 4208 m

Above Chamonix, the tourist resort at the foot of Mont Blanc, rise the granite faces of the Aiguilles de Chamonix. Behind them is the valley of the Mer de Glace glacier, overlooked by Alpine giants, including the Grandes Jorasses and Dent du Géant.

THE BERNESE ALPS

Towards the south-west, before Martigny, the chain of the Bernese Alps narrows to a bare 10 km wide. The Rhône valley separates it from the Valais Alps and the Mont Blanc massif, which presents its characteristic image far in the distance.

THE GLARNER ALPS

At the north-eastern end of the Glarner Alps, south-east of the lake Walensee, is a geologically interesting region, presented as the Sarganserland – Walensee – Glarnerland Geopark.

DENT DU BRENLEIRE, 2353 m, FOLLIERAN, 2340 m, VANIL NOIR, 2389 m

Nowhere else in the Alps are there such well-arranged mountain pastures as in the Bernese Oberland. Long ago the forests were replaced by grassy slopes, which provide the local inhabitants with a basis for survival in the rough nature of these mountain surroundings

THE MATTERHORN / CERVINO / MT. CERVIN, 4478 m

The most characteristic image of the Matterhorn is definitely that from the Swiss side – from the Mattertal valley. For a long time its precipitous north face together with the Eiger and the Walker Spur in the Grandes Jorasses constituted one of the three main climbing problems of the Alps.

241

Adamello-Brenta [ITALY]   N 46° 26' 11" E 11° 04' 06"   ⌖ 3180 m

THE CENTRAL ALPS

Similaun, 3607 m, Hintere Schwärze, 3628 m [ITALY / AUSTRIA]

N 46° 45' 30" E 10° 51' 54"   ♺ 3813 m

Sylvensteinsee, 775 m [GERMANY]

The Allgäuer Alps [AUSTRIA / GERMANY]

N 47° 20' 35" E 10° 08' 56"   Ω 2434 m

The Tessin Alps, Lake Lugano, 271 m [ITALY]

N 45° 50' 06" E 08° 52' 44" ↻ 1447 m

Hohe Kreuzspitze / *Monte Altacroce*, 2743 m [ITALY]

N 46° 56' 34" E 11° 14' 17" ☊ 3768 m

Neuschwanstein Castle, 963 m [GERMANY]

The Miemingergebirge [AUSTRIA]

N 47° 22' 17" E 11° 00' 03"   ☉ 2566 m

Sandstone pyramids [ITALY]

N 46° 31' 35" E 11° 24' 12" ♄ 1475 m

Hochfeiler / *Gran Pilastro*, 3510 m [AUSTRIA / ITALY]

N 46° 59' 15" E 11° 44' 38" ⏛ 3566 m

The Glarner Alps [SWITZERLAND]

N 47° 10' 54" E 08° 44' 15"   ⟳ 1633 m

Zugspitze, 2962 m [GERMANY / AUSTRIA]

N 47° 25' 34" E 11° 04' 06"   ⟲ 3071 m

The Ille valley [GERMANY]

N 47° 29' 13" E 10° 16' 14"   ☉ 1783 m

The Allgäuer Alps [AUSTRIA / GERMANY]

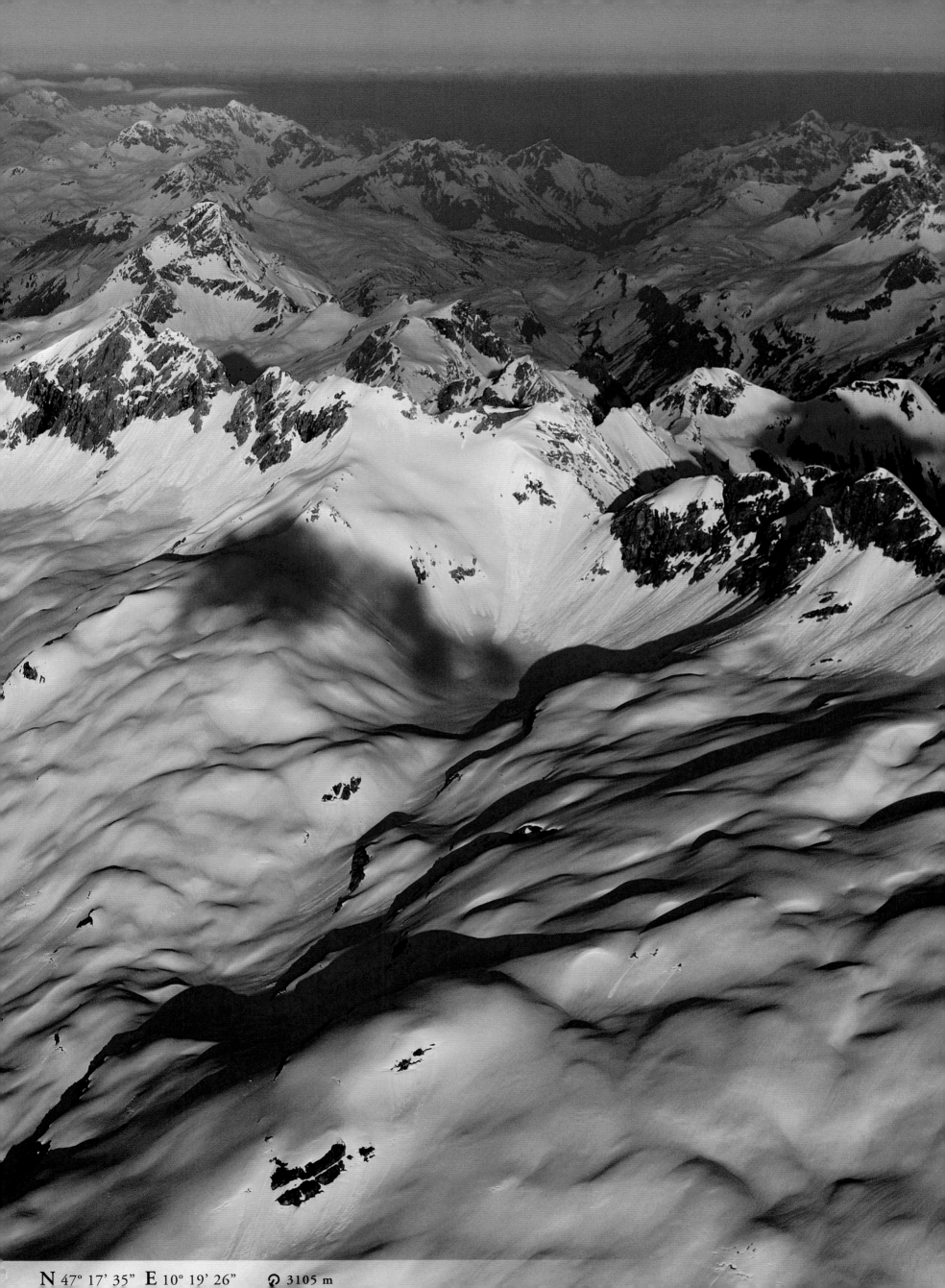

N 47° 17' 35" E 10° 19' 26" 3105 m

The Furka pass, 2431 m [SWITZERLAND]

N 46° 33' 33" E 08° 30' 11" ↻ 3766 m

Samnaungruppe - Silvretta [AUSTRIA / SWITZERLAND]

N 47° 03' 52" E 10° 18' 30" ⟳ 3295 m

Vierwaldstättersee - Lake Lucerne, 434 m [SWITZERLAND]

N 46° 56' 27" E 08° 32' 38" ☊ 2562 m

Biancograt - Piz Bernina, 4049 m [SWITZERLAND]

N 46° 23' 48" E 09° 53' 25" ⟳ 3610 m

Vinschgau / *Val Venosta* [ITALY]

N 46° 37' 22" E 10° 35' 39" ⌀ 1622 m

Weisskugel / *Palla Bianca*, 3739 m [ITALY / AUSTRIA]

N 46° 47' 29" E 10° 43' 28"   ⌖ 3851 m

Lake Silvaplana - St. Moritz [SWITZERLAND]

N 46° 27' 59" E 09° 51' 46" ⊘ 3854 m

Presanella, 3558 m [ITALY]

N 46° 16' 55" E 10° 36' 36" ⏾ 2838 m

Upper Vinschgau [ITALY]

N 46° 43' 44" E 10° 28' 48"   ☺ 3093 m

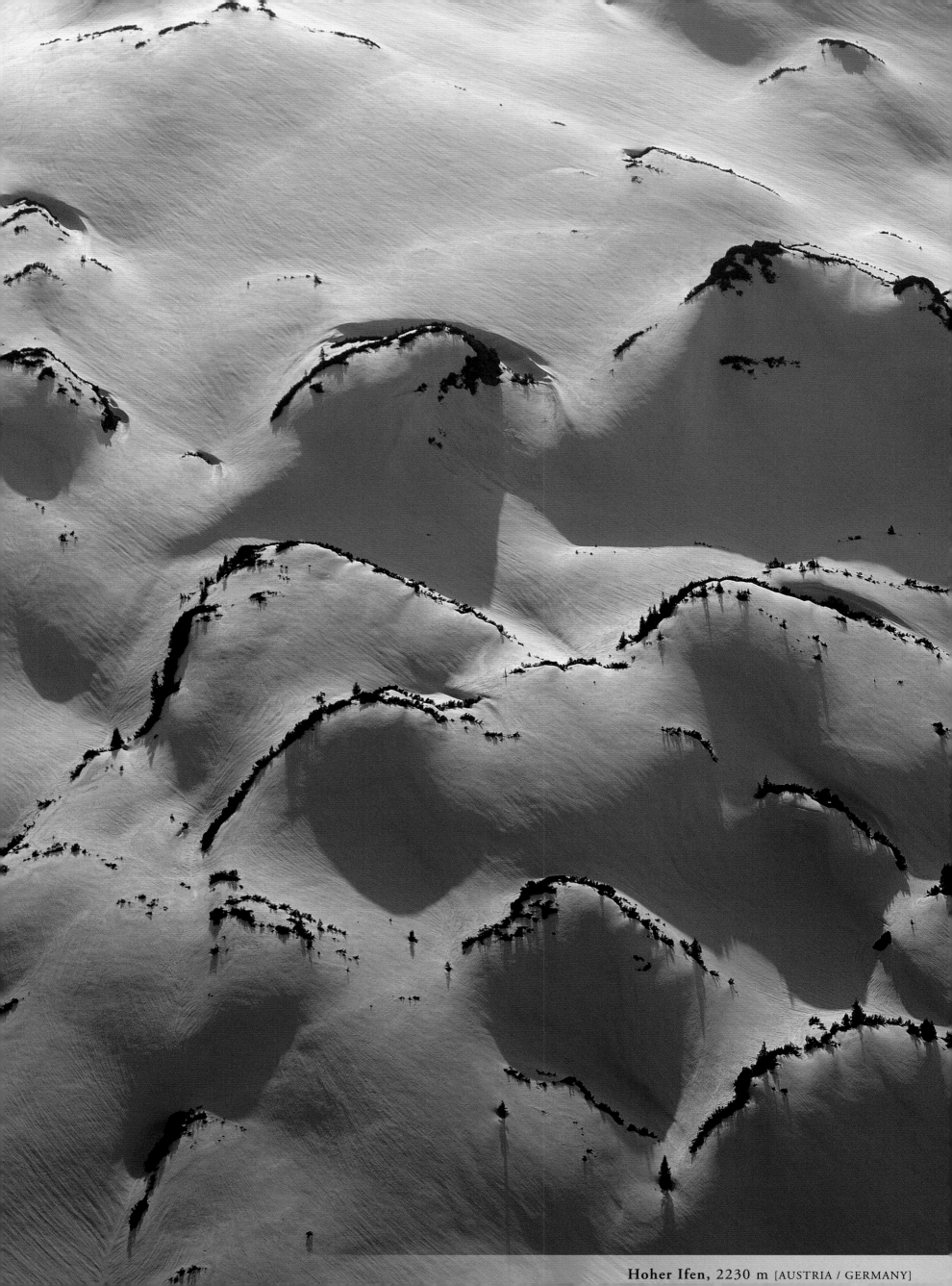

Hoher Ifen, 2230 m [AUSTRIA / GERMANY]

N 47° 21' 41" E 10° 08' 22"   ☉ 2165 m

Como - Lake Como [ITALY]

N 45° 48' 05" E 09° 07' 03"   1360 m

Zugspitze, 2962 m [AUSTRIA / GERMANY]

N 47° 22' 45" E 10° 56' 24"   ☊ 2891 m

Heiterwanger See, Plansee [AUSTRIA]

N 47° 26' 29" E 10° 43' 51" ⋂ 1734 m

The Wettersteingebirge [GERMANY / AUSTRIA]

N 47° 26' 06" E 11° 09' 08" ↻ 2970 m

The Karwendelgebirge [AUSTRIA]

N 47° 31' 31" E 11° 14' 46" ☉ 1921 m

Hoher Riffler, 3168 m [AUSTRIA]

N 47° 08' 18" E 10° 20' 43"   ↻ 3190 m

The Lepontine Alps [ITALY]

N 46° 32' 48" E 08° 30' 23"   ⟲ 3763 m

Bodensee / *Lake Constance* [SWITZERLAND / GERMANY / AUSTRIA]

N 47° 31' 49" E 09° 38' 12"   1417 m

Piz Linard, 3410 m [SWITZERLAND]

N 46° 51' 19" E 10° 03' 26" ↻ 3631 m

The Marienberg / *Monte Maria Monastery*, 1340 m [ITALY]

N 46° 42' 03" E 10° 31' 46"   ☊ 1546 m

Ortler, 3905 m [ITALY]

N 46° 31' 48" E 10° 31' 52"   ↻ 3918 m

Säntis, 2503 m [SWITZERLAND]

N 47° 19' 08" E 09° 28' 52" ↻ 1806 m

Gran Zebrù / *Königspitze*, 3850 m [ITALY]

N 46° 29' 56" E 10° 31' 40"   ☉ 3963 m

The Bergamo Alps [ITALY]

N 45° 42' 12" E 09° 38' 05"   ☉ 1095 m

Piz Cengalo, 3367 m, Piz Badile, 3308 m [SWITZERLAND / ITALY]

N 46° 31' 41" E 09° 20' 24" ⌀ 3239 m

The Bei Laghi Lakes, 2740 m [ITALY]

N 46° 23' 40" E 10° 23' 26" ♇ 3763 m

The Bernina massif [SWITZERLAND]

N 46° 28' 13" E 10° 05' 20"   ⌀ 4270 m

Oberinntal [AUSTRIA]

N 47° 12' 09" E 10° 49' 37"   ☉ 3195 m

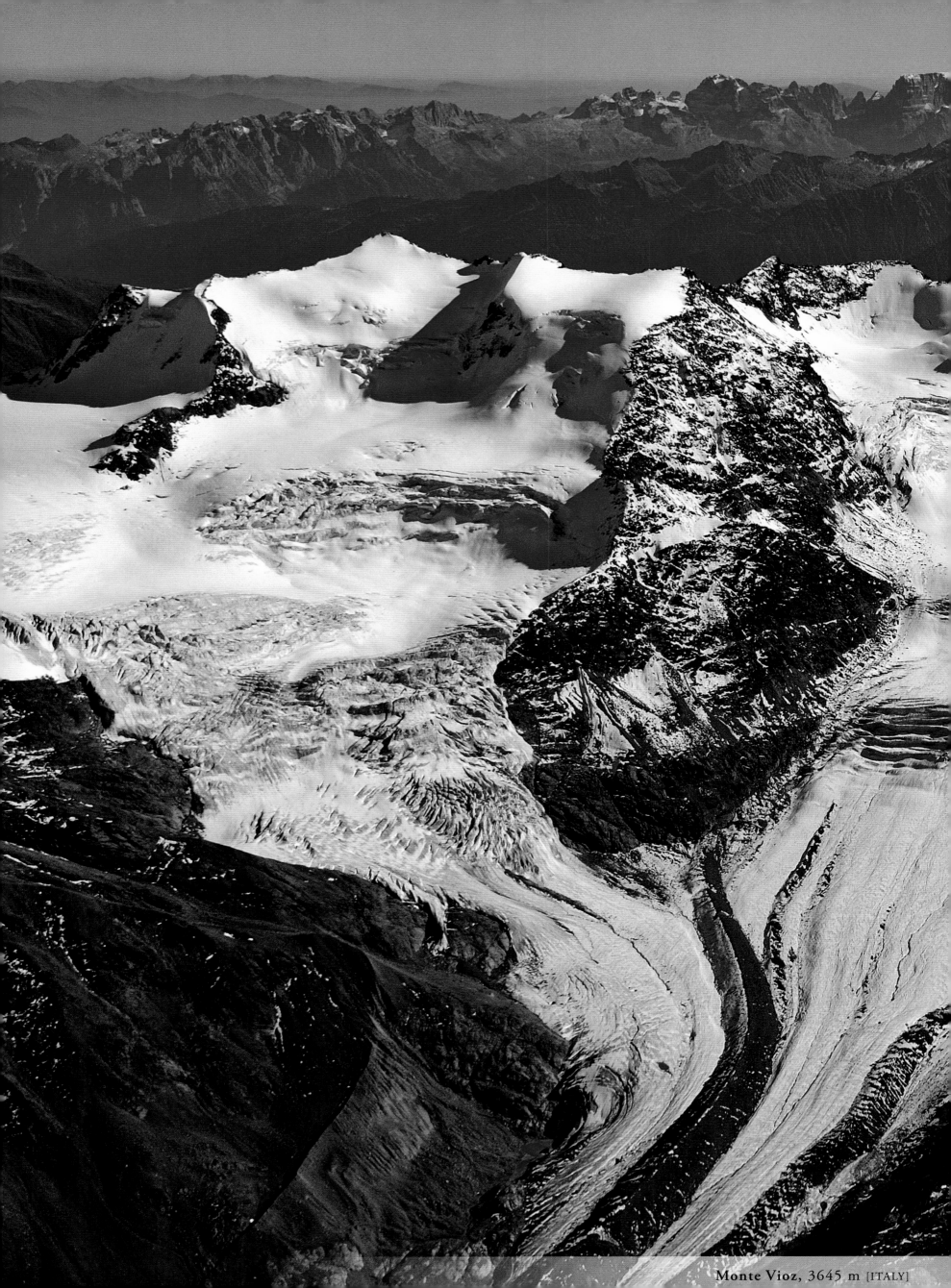

Monte Vioz, 3645 m [ITALY]

N 46° 25' 09" E 10° 33' 35"   ⌀ 4120 m

The Bregaglia massif [ITALY / SWITZERLAND]

N 46° 12' 13" E 09° 45' 43"   ⟳ 3450 m

Piz Quattervals, 3164 m [SWITZERLAND]

N 46° 40' 00" E 10° 03' 46" ☊ 2508 m

The Oberhalbstein valley [SWITZERLAND]

N 46° 23' 11" E 09° 38' 03"   ◯ 4253 m

Kleiner and Grosser Mythen, 1898 m [SWITZERLAND]

N 47° 05' 19" E 08° 37' 41" ↻ 1898 m

Passeierspitze, 3036 m [AUSTRIA]

N 47° 14' 07" E 10° 29' 31" ☉ 2916 m

Parcines / *Partschins,* 630 m [ITALY]

N 46° 39' 19" E 11° 05' 47"   ⟳ 2900 m

The Ötztal Alps [AUSTRIA / ITALY]

N 46° 46' 26" E 10° 57' 20"   ☾ 3827 m

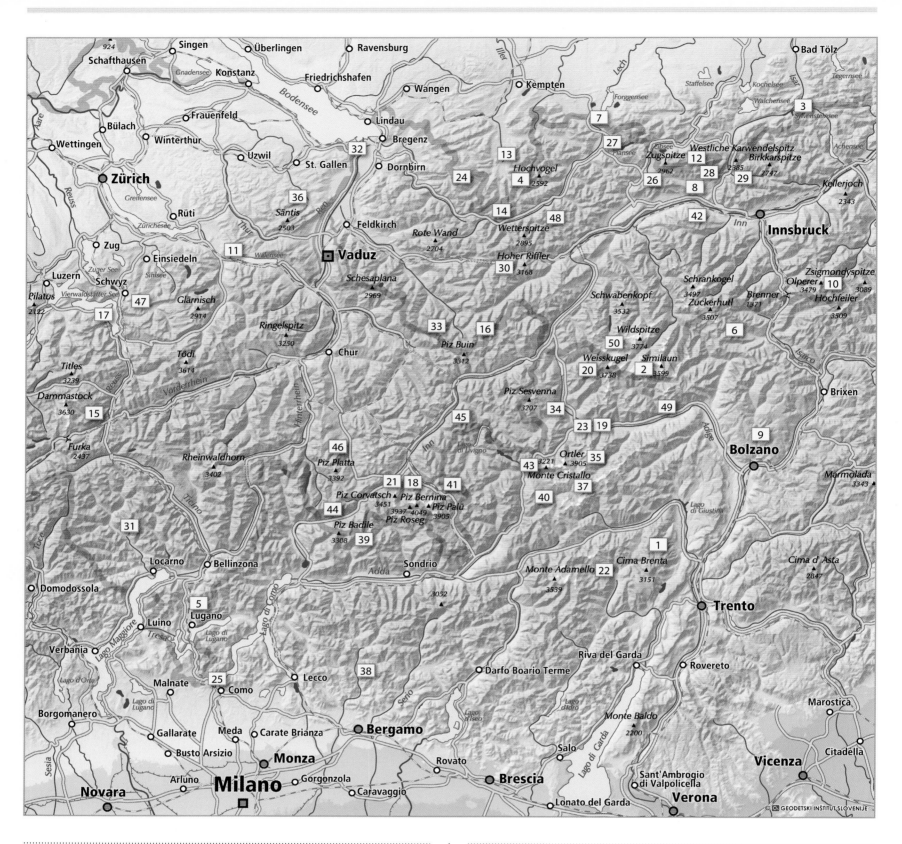

Part of the map "The Central Alps" showing locations in Switzerland, Austria, Italy and Germany including Zürich, Innsbruck, Bolzano, Milano, Trento, Verona, Bergamo, Brescia and numerous mountain peaks and lakes.

ADAMELLO - BRENTA

1 Part of the Southern Limestone Alps is protected in the Adamello-Brenta Regional Park. On account of the great height difference – a good 3000 m, the many glaciers, lakes, waterfalls and forests, it has a very diversified environment, in which the brown bear also lives, having been re-introduced here from the Slovene forests.

SYLVENSTEINSEE

3 Sylvensteinsee is the second reservoir after Walchensee for producing electricity and preventing floods on the Isar. This river has its source in the Hinterau valley in the Karwendel massif, and it flows through Munich into the Danube. The Isar carries with it silt and gravel, which it deposits in the reservoir.

2 Similaun is the sixth highest summit in Austria and the well-known holy mountain of Tyrol. Across its Tisenjoch and Niederjoch Glaciers run traverses several millenia old from the southern valley of Schnalstal to the northern Ötztal valley. In 1991 the 5300-year-old mummified remains of Ötzi – the Iceman – were found in the ice on the Tisenjoch plateau at an altitude of 3210 m.

SIMILAUN, 3607 m
HINTERE SCHWÄRZE, 3628 m

THE ALLGÄUER ALPS

4 On the German-Austrian border near Oberstdorf are the northern limestone two-thousanders of the Allgäuer Alps. This is also the southernmost point of Germany. The highest summit in the chain is Grosser Krottenkopf (2657 m).

THE TESSIN ALPS, LAKE LUGANO

The Swiss-Italian border twice crosses Lake Lugano, which makes fjord-like indentations into the foothills of the Tessin Alps. The motorways that cross the high passes of San Bernardino and San Gottardo run past the town of Lugano, situated on the lake's northern shore.

KREUZSPITZE, 2743 m

The easternmost part of the Ötztal Alps, between the passes of Timmelsjoch (2474 m) and Jaufenpass (2099 m), comprises the mountains above the Passeiertal valley. Kreuzspitze rises above the Ratschingstal valley. West of this peak stands Schneeberg, where there is a museum of the lead and zinc mine with its 800-year-old history.

NEUSCHWANSTEIN CASTLE

Neuschwanstein Castle is one of the most characteristic in Germany. It is situated on the northern slopes of the Ammergebirge near Füssen in southern Bavaria. Construction of the castle started in 1869, in the time of King Ludwig II of Bavaria, on the site of two ruined mansions.

THE MIEMINGERGEBIRGE

The small Miemingergebirge range stands west of Innsbruck and south-west of the Wettersteingebirge. The twin summits of Hohen Munde (2662 m) rise above the Leutaschtal valley, with Hochwand (2719 m) in front.

SANDSTONE PYRAMIDS

North of Bolzano/Bozen, in the Finsterbach valley, on a hillside near Ritten/Renon there are sandstone pillars surrounded by forest that have been formed through the centuries by erosion and other weather factors. The highest ones are pyramids which have kept a rock on top for the longest time; this protects them from the action of water.

HOCHFEILER / GRAN PILASTRO, 3510 m

Hochfeiler is the highest mountain in the Zillertal Alps. Its north face offers climbers classic, demanding ice routes. The waters from under the northern glaciers gather in the big reservoir Schlegeisstausee above the Zillertal valley.

THE GLARNER ALPS

South-east of Zürich grassy plains with numerous lakes gradually give way to the mountain chain of the Glarner Alps. Sihlsee is a reservoir formed behind a concrete dam in 1937. If the dam should collapse, it is estimated that an 8-metre-high wave of water would burst upon Zurich.

ZUGSPITZE, 2962 m

Although this summit receives a massive influx of tourists due to the highest ski centre in Germany being located there, plus the mountain railway and two cableways, it is possible to reach it on foot by following numerous secured routes from Germany or Austria.

THE ILLE VALLEY

Seven streams flow down from seven valleys in the Allgäuer Alps, in the southernmost part of Germany, and combine to form the River Ille at Oberstdorf. The Ille valley is well-known as a sports and tourist region with exceptionally well-preserved countryside.

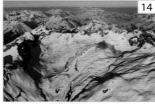

THE ALLGÄUER ALPS

The Lechtal valley borders the Allgäuer and Lechtal mountain ranges. The Allgäuer Alps lie on the border between Austria and Germany; their highest summit is Bockkarkopf (2608 m). The famous Heilbronner route leads over the surrounding two-thousanders.

THE FURKA PASS, 2431 m

Above the slopes where the road winds towards the Furka pass lie the Urner/Uri Alps. In the foreground rises the third highest summit, Galenstock (3586 m), while the highest one, Dammastock (3630 m), hides behind it. The south-eastern glaciers of both peaks supply most of the ice of the Rhône Glacier, below which rises the great Alpine river of that name.

THE SILVRETTA - SAMNAUNGRUPPE

On the Austrian - Swiss border lies the Samnaun mountain group. Gondolas serving one of the biggest skiing terrains in the Alps lead up into the heart of three-thousanders. The Silvretta Arena connects the Austrian Ischgl and the Swiss Samnaun. In the background is Muttler (3294 m) and behind that Ortler (3509 m).

VIERWALDSTÄTTERSEE / LAKE LUCERNE, 434 m

This lake lies below the western slopes of the Glarner Alps, on the border of three cantons. It has a branching, fjord-like shape, a surface area of over 113 km² and its greatest depth is 214 m. It is fed mainly by the River Reuss in its eastern arm and its outlet is the same river at the town of Lucerne.

BIANCOGRAT – PIZ BERNINA, 4049 m

Piz Bernina is the highest peak of the Bernina massif in the Engadine Alps. Biancograt is an ideal snow and ice ridge, which one of the best-known climbing routes follows. The Tschierva and Morteratsch Glaciers are a rich source of water for the River Inn, which rises near St. Moritz, while the waters from the southern glaciers flow into the Po Plain.

VINSCHGAU / VAL VENOSTA

At the point where the valleys below the Reschenpass, Offenpass and Stelvio pass meet there is a broad plain of river-borne alluvial deposits, where the inhabitants of Oris, Cengles and Glurns have cultivated farmlands.

WEISSKUGEL / PALLA BIANCA, 3739 m

Weisskugel/Palla Bianca is the second highest summit in the Ötztal Alps. The easiest access is by the Val Senales/Schnalstal valley from the ski centre of Maso Corto/Kurzras. From the peak the Hintereis Glacier descends northwards into the Vent valley at Sölden.

LAKE SILVAPLANA – ST. MORITZ

In the Oberengadin valley, below the Bernina massif and the Rhaetian Alps, rise the headwaters of the 500-km-long River Inn. The Oberengadin with its celebrated tourist centre of St. Moritz and the Alpine lakes Silvaplana and Sils has a road connection with the Bregaglia valley via the Maloja pass (1815 m).

PRESANELLA, 3558 m

The mountain ridge of Adamello-Presanella lies south of the Ötztal Alps, from which it is separated by the Tonale pass, west of the Brenta group, from which it is separated by the Campo Carlo Magno pass, and east of the Bergamo Alps, from which it is separated by the Val Camonica valley.

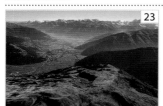

UPPER VINSCHGAU

The upper part of the Vinschgau valley is an extensive plain where the mountain torrents from under Ortler and Weisskugel in the west Ötztal range and from the Müstair valley have deposited their alluvia. Transit traffic also travels along these valleys to the Swiss Engadine, to the valley of the River Inn and to the ski centre of Bormio to the south.

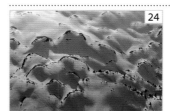

HOHER IFEN, 2230 m

The karst plateau below the summit of Hoher Ifen in the Allgäuer Alps, on the border between Germany and Austria, hides Stone Age remains. Today these slopes above the Kleinwalsertal valley provide a densely equipped ski terrain.

COMO – LAKE COMO

The town of Como in Lombardy lies on the south-western arm of Lake Como. This area was settled as early as the Bronze Age. The densely populated southern foothills of the Valais and Lepontine Alps, which gradually descend to the Po Plain, manage to shake off fog, smog and clouds only a few times in the year.

ZUGSPITZE, 2962 m

Zugspitze is Germany's highest peak, situated on the German-Austrian border in the region of Garmisch-Partenkirchen, from where the mountain railway Zugspitzbahn leads to the summit. There are also two gondolas reaching the top of the mountain: one from the German lake Eibsee and the other is the Austrian Tiroler Zugspitzbahn.

HEITERWANGER SEE, PLANSEE

South-east of Heiterwang and below Haneller (2341 m) in the Ammergauergebirge lies the lake Heiterwanger See, which is connected with the lake Plansee by a canal over 300 m long. The water from the lakes enters the Klein Plansee and the Arcbach stream, which flows into the River Lech near Reutte in Tyrol.

THE WETTERSTEINGEBIRGE

The Wettersteingebirge is an isolated mountain group with Zugspitze as the highest summit. To the south the Leutascher valley separates it from the Miemingergebirge. The River Leutascher foams through a picturesque gorge to Mittenwald in the Isar valley. To the north is the valley with the ski centre of Garmisch-Partenkirchen.

THE KARWENDELGEBIRGE

The River Isar has carved its way between the high ridges of the Wetterstein range and the Karwendelgebirge rising to the east. Past the small village of Krün the view opens up to the summits of this biggest chain of the Northern Limestone Alps, to the north of Innsbruck. The highest mountain is Birkkarspitze (2749 m).

HOHER RIFFLER, 3168 m

The Verwallgruppe is a mountain group between the Lechtal Alps in the north, the Samnaungruppe in the south-east and the Silvrettagruppe in the south-west. The highest summit is Hoher Riffler with two glaciers, which descend along the northern and north-eastern slopes into the Stanzertal valley.

THE LEPONTINE ALPS

West of the St. Gotthard pass the Lepontine mountain ridges extend along the Swiss-Italian border. In the foreground above the Rotonda Glacier is Pizzo Rotondo (3192 m), while the valley on the left leads towards the Novena saddle and the artificial lake Togia. In the background are the Ofenhorn (3235 m) and the Blinnenhorn (3374 m), and on the horizon the Monte Rosa massif.

BODENSEE / LAKE CONSTANCE

Bodensee/Lake Constance, which was formed in the glacial basin of the Rhine Glacier, is shared by Germany, Switzerland and Austria. It is mainly fed by the Alpine Rhine, which flows into the lake at Bregenz. The south-eastern backdrop is formed by the Bregenzerwald range.

PIZ LINARD, 3410 m

Piz Linard, a pyramid-shaped mountain north of the Inn valley, the Engadine, is the highest one in the Silvretta massif. In the background are the Ortler and Bernina ranges.

THE MARIENBERG / MONTE MARIA MONASTERY

The Marienberg Monastery in the Vinschgau valley, is the biggest Benedictine monastery in Europe. It was founded by the Counts of Tarasp in the 12th century. Today the monastery represents the spiritual, cultural and economic centre of the upper Vinschgau valley.

ORTLER, 3905 m

South-west of the Vinschgau valley lies the Ortler group, in the Stelvio/Stilfser Joch National Park. The highest mountain, Ortler, is covered in glaciers right to its summit; these descend into the Trafoi and Sulden valleys. In 1990 WWI cannon were discovered just below the summit, a reminder of the battles between the Italian and Austro-Hungarian armies.

SÄNTIS, 2503 m

Säntis is a panoramic summit in the Appenzeller Alps near the Austrian border. To the east the Bregenzerwald range can be seen, Rätikon in the south-east, the Glarner Alps in the south and Bodensee in the north.

GRAN ZEBRÙ / KÖNIGSPITZE, 3850 m

From the top of Ortler the ridge continues towards the south-east, reaching its highest point on Gran Zebrù/Königspitze. There is no simple route to this summit; the easiest access is from the Casati mountain hut on the south side from the saddle between Gran Zebrù and Monte Cevedale.

**PIZ CENGALO, 3367 m
PIZ BADILE, 3308 m**

The Bregaglia group lies on the Swiss-Italian border, south-west of the Bernina massif. In terms of alpinism, the most interesting mountain is Piz Badile with its north-east face, one of the six biggest north faces in the Alps. In 1937 the famous alpinist Cassin with his co-climbers established a big classic route here.

THE BERNINA MASSIF

The Bernina group with the familiar summits of Piz Palü (3905 m) and Piz Bernina (4049 m) can be encircled by taking roads through the southern valley of Valtellina over the Bernina pass (2323 m) into the Oberengadin valley and over the Maloja pass (1815 m) into the Bregaglia valley.

MONTE VIOZ

Monte Vioz, together with its neighbours Punta Taviela and Punta San Matteo, rises in the southern part of the Ortler range in the Stelvio/Stilfser Joch National Park. The Forni Glacier descends over the north-western slopes into the Valle dei Forni valley.

PIZ QUATTERVALS, 3164 m

Above the Oberengadin valley, where the River Inn arises near St. Moritz, lie the Engadine Alps, partly included in the almost 100-year-old Swiss National Park. The park comprises the mountainous region between the Oberengadin and Unterengadin, the Ofenpass and the Italian border. The larch tree-line lies at an altitude of roughly 2200 m.

KLEINER AND GROSSER MYTHEN, 1898 m

North of the lake Vierwaldstättersee stand three solitary peaks, Grosser and Kleiner Mythen and Haggenspitz, which form a special feature of the landscape. These geologically interesting mountains are a favourite destination when local people go for a trip.

PARTSCHINS / PARCINES

A few kilometres west of Meran in the mouth of the Vinschgau valley/Val Venosta, below the Ötztal Alps lies Parcines, surrounded by vineyards. Above the village rises Mt. Texel and the Natural Parc Texelgruppe/Gruppo di Tessa Park.

THE BERGAMO ALPS

North of Bergamo in Lombardy, these slopes rise up towards the Bergamo Alps/Alpe Orobie with their highest summit Pizzo di Coca (3052 m).

THE BEI LAGHI LAKES, 2740 m

The Stelvio/Stilfserjoch National Park is the biggest in the Alps and was founded in 1935. Lying in the region of the Ortler-Cevedale massif, its highest point is Ortler (3905 m) and the lowest in the Laces valley (650 m). The park is rich in flora and fauna, with big glaciers and numerous lakes. The Bei Laghi lakes with their varied hues lie on the plateau south of Bormio.

OBERINNTAL

West of Innsbruck the River Inn winds out from the embrace of the Lechtal Alps, the Verwallgruppe and the Samnaunberge to flow through the Oberinntal valley. The Miemingergebirge range is separated from the Lechtal Alps by the Fernpass mountain pass (1216 m).

THE BREGAGLIA MASSIF

The Bregaglia group lies on the Italian-Swiss border, as a south-western extension of the Bernina group. The granite summits of Piz Badile (3308 m), Piz Cengalo (3367 m) and Monte Disgrazia (3678 m) provide supreme challenges to the world's best climbers.

THE OBERHALBSTEIN VALLEY

Above the Oberengadin valley, where the River Inn arises near St. Moritz, lie the Engadine Alps, partly included in the almost 100-year-old Swiss National Park. The park comprises the mountainous region between the Oberengadin and Unterengadin, the Ofenpass and the Italian border. The larch tree-line lies at an altitude of roughly 2200 m.

PASSEIERSPITZE, 3036 m

Passeierspitze, the "king of the Lechtal Alps", is also the highest peak in the Northern Limestone Alps. Only 7 km east of the summit, the town of Landeck lies in the Inn valley. Passeierspitze was first climbed by the rope-team Specht-Siess in 1869.

THE ÖTZTAL ALPS

The glaciers from Seelenkogel/Cima delle Anime (3469 m) and Hohe Wilde/Cima dell'Altissima (3480 m) descend into the Obergurgl valley and still further into the Ötztal valley. On the other side, steep mountain faces plunge southwards into the Vinschgau valley.

The Schladminger Tauern [AUSTRIA]　　　　N 47° 15' 50" E 13° 29' 18"　　3143 m

THE EASTERN ALPS

Jôf di Montasio, 2753 m [ITALY]

N 46° 22' 07" E 13° 34' 06" ⟳ 3305 m

Watzmann, 2713 m [GERMANY]

N 47° 34' 29" E 12° 56' 52" ⊘ 3105 m

Antelao, 3264 m [ITALY]

N 46° 12' 09" E 12° 05' 56"   ⌀ 3005 m

Grossglockner, 3798 m [AUSTRIA]

N 47° 05' 49" E 12° 44' 35"   4111 m

Schlern / *Sciliar*, 2563 m [ITALY]

N 46° 31' 26" E 11° 33' 14" ⌀ 2715 m

Storžič, 2132 m [SLOVENIA]

N 46° 23' 17" E 14° 20' 18" ☽ 2516 m

The Dachstein range [AUSTRIA]

N 47° 25' 21" E 13° 30' 05" ⌖ 1677 m

The Nockberge National Park [AUSTRIA]

N 46° 53' 24" E 13° 36' 21" ⍉ 2991 m

Hochkönig, 2941 m [AUSTRIA]

N 47° 24' 57" E 13° 09' 39"   ⋂ 2006 m

The Dolomites [ITALY]

N 46° 48' 25" E 12° 17' 10" ⟳ 2954 m

The Nieder Tauern [AUSTRIA]

N 47° 20' 36" E 14° 30' 08"   ⌖ 2677 m

Sorapis, 3205 m [ITALY]

N 46° 30' 08" E 12° 15' 39"   ⟳ 3335 m

The Lienzer Dolomites [AUSTRIA]

N 46° 45' 21" E 12° 43' 26" ☉ 3587 m

Tofana di Rozes, 3225 m, Tofana di Mezzo, 3244 m [ITALIJA]

N 46° 30' 57" E 12° 02' 51"   ↻ 2910 m

Komna, 1640 m [SLOVENIA]

N 46° 17' 58" E 13° 46' 37" ⟳ 2711 m

Le Vette Feltrine [ITALIA]

N 46° 06' 21" E 11° 52' 50"   3237 m

Schaffberg, 1783 m [AUSTRIA]

N 47° 42' 41" E 13° 23' 54"   ☊ 1846 m

Krn, 2244 m [SLOVENIJA]

N 46° 15' 29" E 13° 37' 45"   3815 m

Gruppo del Rinaldo [ITALIA]

N 46° 36' 32" E 12° 41' 25"   2911 m

Viš, 2666 m [ITALIJA]

N 46° 28' 04" E 13° 31' 21" ⍉ 2610 m

Cima di Terrarossa / *Roterdspitze*, 2665 m [ITALIJA]

N 46° 31' 22" E 11° 41' 15" ☉ 2925 m

Totes Gebirge [AVSTRIJA]

N 47° 46' 13" E 14° 05' 34" ⦾ 2540 m

Tri Cine, 2999 m [ITALIJA]

N 46° 35' 38" E 12° 18' 29" ↻ 3311 m

Hoher Dachstein, 2995 m [AVSTRIJA]

N 47° 29' 25" E 13° 36' 05" ⟳ 3111 m

Begunjščica, 2060 m [SLOVENIJA]

Pale di San Martino [ITALIJA]

N 46° 10' 35" E 11° 49' 35" ☉ 3542 m

Grossvenediger, 3667 m [AUSTRIA]

N 47° 05' 09" E 12° 29' 31" ⟳ 4099 m

La Valle / *La Val* [ITALY]

N 46° 39' 52" E 11° 54' 46" ☉ 3115 m

Marmolada, 3343 m, Cimon della Pala, 3184 m [ITALY]

N 46° 11' 31" E 11° 45' 32" Ω 3365 m

Hohe Warte / *Monte Coglians*, 2780 m [AUSTRIA / ITALY]

N 46° 34' 10" E 12° 51' 51" ⌀ 2935 m

Hochalmspitze, 3360 m [AUSTRIA]

N 46° 55' 42" E 13° 17' 32"   3437 m

Marmolada, 3343 m [ITALY]

N 46° 30' 05" E 11° 53' 04"   ↻ 3386 m

Kočna, 2475 m, Grintovec, 2558 m [SLOVENIA]

N 46° 17' 19" E 14° 35' 08"   Ø 2562 m

Gemona, 217 m [ITALY]

N 46° 14' 13" E 13° 07' 53" ⟳ 2691 m

Škrlatica, 2740 m [SLOVENIA]

N 46° 27' 32" E 13° 44' 57"   ↻ 3011 m

Hochgall / *Collalto*, 3436 m [AUSTRIA / ITALY]

N 46° 56' 04" E 12° 09' 10" ⌖ 3784 m

Dösental [AUSTRIA]

N 46° 58' 17" E 13° 10' 45"   ⟳ 3600 m

Civetta, 3220 m [ITALY]

N 46° 25' 09" E 12° 00' 35" ✪ 3201 m

The Gesäuse National Park [AUSTRIA]

N 47° 35' 08" E 14° 29' 30" ⟳ 2493 m

Triglav, 2864 m [SLOVENIA]

N 46° 25' 09" E 13° 44' 45" ⟲ 3241 m

Schlern / *Sciliar*, 2563 m [ITALY]

N 46° 31' 26" E 11° 33' 14"   ↻ 2715 m

Grossglockner, 3798 m [AUSTRIA]

N 47° 01' 08" E 12° 42' 34" ☊ 3791 m

Monte Pelmo, 3168 m, Monte Civetta, 3220 m [ITALY]

Mala Baba, 2018 m, **Ojstrica**, 2350 m [SLOVENIA]

N 46° 23' 57" E 14° 31' 00" ♌ 2267 m

The Rosengarten / *Catinaccio group* [ITALY]

N 46° 32' 34" E 11° 39' 20" ⟳ 3359 m

Bled, 475 m [SLOVENIA]

N 46° 21' 52" E 14° 04' 58"   ⟳ 1019 m

Val di Fassa [ITALY]

N 46° 22' 40" E 11° 38' 13" ⦾ 3390 m

The Karavanke / *Karawanken* [SLOVENIA / AUSTRIA]

N 46° 28' 23" E 14° 07' 14" ☉ 2405 m

The Totes Gebirge [AUSTRIA]

N 47° 41' 24" E 13° 59' 09"   ↻ 2415 m

The Seckauer Tauern [AUSTRIA]

N 47° 19' 29" E 14° 40' 41" ⏾ 2439 m

The Dolomites [ITALY]

N 46° 25' 13" E 12° 37' 15"   ♋ 3308 m

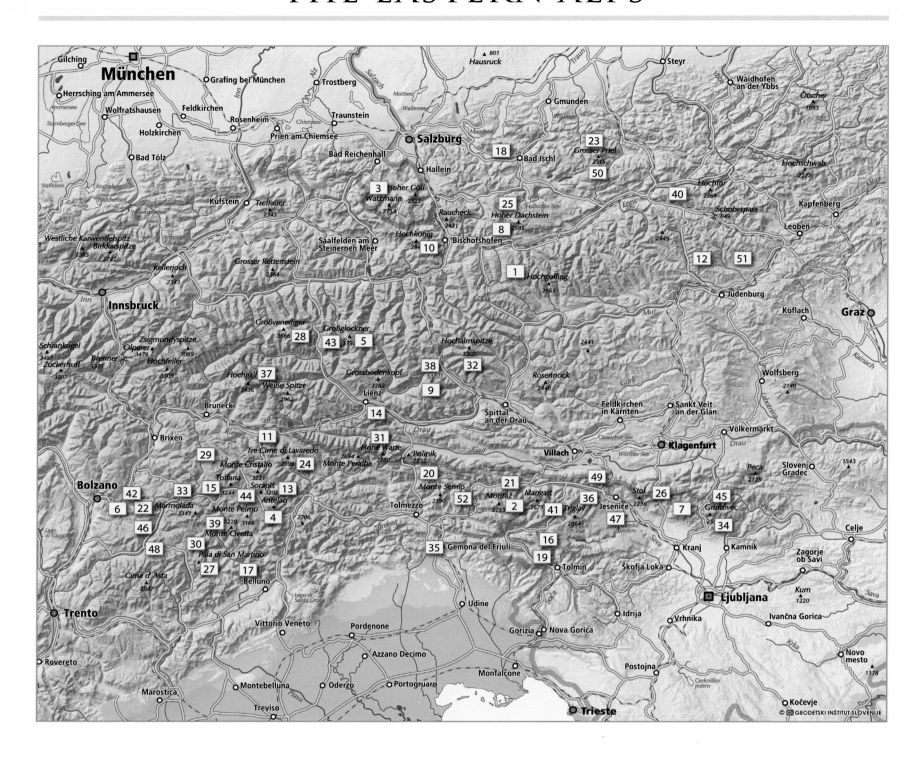

1

The northern part of the Niedere Tauern includes the Schladminger Tauern range, which lies on the right bank of the River Enns opposite the south faces of Dachstein. It is divided from the Hohe Tauern by the headwaters region of the River Mur. The highest peak is Hochgolling (2863 m), which is also the highest in the Niedere Tauern.

THE SCHLADMINGER TAUERN

2

Jôf di Montasio is the second highest summit in the Julian Alps and the highest summit in the Western Julians. It is separated from the Monte Canin/Kanin massif by the Val Rio del Lago valley rising to the Sella Nevea saddle, from where the usual approach leads up via Altipiano del Montasio. In the background are the multitudinous peaks of the Carnian Alps.

JÔF DI MONTASIO, 2753 m

3

Numerous legends and traditions about its origin are woven around the highest summit and symbol of Bavaria. In 1800 the first ascent was soloed by the Slovene alpinist, Valentin Stanič, who also measured its altitude. Below the mountain's east face lies a hidden jewel, the lake Königssee. The Watzmann massif forms the central region of the Berchtesgaden National Park.

WATZMANN, 2713 m

4

Its pyramidal bulk and second greatest altitude have given this mountain the epithet "King of the Dolomites". It rises up in the Antelao-Sorapis group, south-east of Cortina d'Ampezzo, and joins with the Marmarola group north of the Cadore valley. For climbers the greatest attraction is its south face.

ANTELAO, 3264 m

GROSSGLOCKNER, 3798 m

The highest mountain and the symbol of Austria lies in the Hohe Tauern and the national park of the same name. The summit was first reached by local climbers from Heiligenblut in 1800. The Pasterze Glacier below the north-east faces is a typical example of rapidly melting ice and glacial retreat caused by climate change.

STORŽIČ, 2132 m

Storžič is a solitary summit belonging to the Kamnik-Savinja Alps. Rising in the far western part of the range, it is separated from the central part by the deep Kokra valley. Behind is the bulky Kalški greben (2039 m), a southern spur of the group that links the Krvavec ski centre with the highest peak of these Alps, Grintovec.

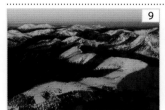

THE NOCKBERGE NATIONAL PARK

North of Villach, in the western part of the geologically ancient Gurktaler Alps, lies the Nockberge National Park. The region had been intended for intensive skiing and tourist development but the local population prevented destructive plans in the referendum of 1980. The national park was founded seven years later.

THE DOLOMITES

The Carnian Alps end with the Drau valley at Toblach. Southwards the view embraces a throng of towers, the cloud-piercing sharp peaks of the Sexten Dolomites. The most immediately recognizable are the Zwölferkofel (3094 m) and Tre Cime (2999 m) groups.

SORAPIS, 3205 m

The Antelao-Sorapis-Marmarole group, lying between the Cadore and Ampezzo valleys, is one of the most rugged in the Dolomites. Summits like Sorapis and its neighbour Antelao (3264 m) have difficult access and demand some climbing expertise. Three glaciers are hidden in the northern faces of Sorapis, though their days are numbered due to global warming.

TOFANA DI ROZES, 3225 m
TOFANA DI MEZZO, 3244 m

This entire massif lies west of Cortina d'Ampezzo, its majestic south faces plunging into the valley which leads to the Falzarego pass, while in the east the Travenanzes valley separates the massif from the Lavarella group. Tofana di Rozes with its mighty south face, which includes eight pillars, is a demanding alpinist goal.

LE VETTE FELTRINE

Above the Piave valley by Belluno rises the mountain group Le Vette Feltrine, which lies in the Dolomiti Bellunesi National Park. The park continues eastwards to the Schiara group. It was established in 1990 with the aim of protecting the natural and cultural landscape, which in this region has been shaped since prehistoric times.

KRN, 2244 m

This marvellous mountain in the Julian Alps above the Soča/Isonzo valley symbolizes the most tragic part of the history of the Alps. During the years 1915 -1917 a succession of battles were waged on these high ridges between the Austro-Hungarian and Italian armies, bringing death to several hundreds of thousands of soldiers.

SCHLERN / SCILIAR, 2563 m

The grassy plateau of this typical mountain on the eastern threshold of the Rosengarten group, north-east of Bolzano, has a special place in the history of South Tyrol. Religious rituals were carried out here in the Bronze Age. The remains of this cultic site are still visible and represent the highest prehistoric place of sacrifice in the Alps.

THE DACHSTEIN RANGE

The south faces of the Dachstein massif, falling into the Enns valley, face the mountains above Schladming, to the north-east they border on the Totes Gebirge, to the west on the Tennen Gebirge. Below the northern slopes the lake Hallstätter See lies hidden. In the foreground is the hillside tourist village of Filzmoos, with Rötelstein (2247 m) rising above; this offers fine views.

HOCHKÖNIG, 2941 m

The Hochkönig range is the south-eastern outlier of the Berchtesgaden Alps, which are connected with the Steinernes Meer via the Torscharte saddle (2246 m). The southern and eastern slopes descend to the Salzach valley, with its sports tourist centre of Bischofshofen.

THE NIEDER TAUERN

East of the Pölstal valley the Nieder Tauern gradually lose height. The view opens up across the panoramic summit of Griesstein (2023 m) northwards to the Ennstaler Alps, the Gesäuse National Park and the Eisenerzer Alps.

THE LIENZER DOLOMITES

The Lienzer Dolomites are a small group of mountains with precipitous faces between the Drau and Gailtal valleys. They represent the western end of the Gailtaler Alps. The highest peak is Grosse Sandspitze (2770 m).

KOMNA

Komna is a high-altitude karst plateau in the Julian Alps, lying in the Triglav National Park and providing a passage from the Bohinj valley over into the Bovec valley. It is partially covered by spruce and larch forests. In spring it offers ideal terrain for ski touring.

SCHAFBERG, 1783 m

Between the lakes Wolfgangsee to the south and Mondsee to the north in the Salzkammergut stands Schafberg, with a railway up it constructed in 1893. Today the old steam locomotive as a tourist attraction still overcomes 1190 metres height distance in 45 minutes.

**THE CARNIAN ALPS
– GRUPPO DEL RINALDO**

The Carnian Alps are part of the Southern Limestone Alps, and gained their name from the Roman province of Carnia. They represent a natural boundary between Austria and Italy, with the Gailtal valley to the north and the Val Canale valley to the south. The massif is separated from the Dolomites by the Piave valley.

JÔF FUART, 2666 m

This mountain and Jôf di Montasio are symbols of the Western Julian Alps. They are separated from the Monte Canin/Kanin range by the Val Raccolana and Val Rio del Lago valleys, which join on the Sella Nevea saddle. The north faces of Jôf Fuart, intersected in their upper third by the Via Eterna ledges, plunge into the Val Saisera valley and face the Carnian Alps on the other side.

THE TOTES GEBIRGE

The Totes Gebirge are the last limestone bulwark with summits surpassing 2000 metres before the Alps, via the Kalkalpen National Park in the north-east, give way to the broad Danube valley at Linz. This interesting karst region boasts the Schönberg cave system, 125 km long and 1070 m deep.

HOHER DACHSTEIN, 2995 m

Hoher Dachstein is the highest point of the Northern Limestone Alps. The whole massif, which consists of Dachstein limestone, is characterized by numerous karst phenomena, including abysses. The upper slopes are covered by glaciers, with organized high-altitude skiing areas.

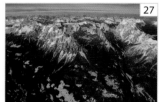

PALE DI SAN MARTINO

The Pale group is one of the biggest in the Dolomites. Its throng of pillars, faces and ridges rises from a 2600-metre-high plateau – Altopiano. The massif is surrounded by the deep gorges of the rivers Cordevole, Cismon and Biois. The western part of the group is protected as the Pale di San Martino Nature Park.

LA VALLE / LA VAL

The Ladin valleys La Valle and Val di Marebbe lie in the north-eastern part of the Alpe di Fanes group, a karstified plateau-like range, which is divided from the Tofana group by the Tadega pass.

MONTE COGLIANS / HOHE WARTE, 2780 m

This is the highest mountain in the Carnian Alps. The southern slopes are more friendly and cannot be compared with the sheer north faces. On the right, western side is the Passo Volaia/Wolayer Pass, behind which lies the lake of the same name, while the eastern side drops down to the Monte Croce/Plöcken Pass.

MARMOLADA, 3343 m

Marmolada, the loftiest peak in the Dolomites, has two aspects. The broad south face is a challenge for the world's best rock climbers while the gentle northern slopes, glacier-covered to the top, provide extensive skiing terrain. A cableway on the northern side reaches the summit but winter sports profit comes at a heavy price – the destruction of the natural environment.

GEMONA

The Alpine rivers Tagliamento and Fella, which join near Tolmezzo, flow from the mountain embrace of the Western Julian Alps and the Carnian Alps by the town of Gemona, situated on extensive river alluvia. The left bank of the Fella, right up to the Slovene border, is protected as the Prealpi Giulie Nature Park.

CIMA DI TERRAROSSA / ROTERDSPITZE, 2665 m

The Alpe di Siusi/Seiser Alm is a plateau region in the western part of the Dolomites between Val Gardena to the north, Schlern to the north-west and Sassolungo to the north-east. Cima di Terrarossa is a ridge extension of the Schlern plateau, which ends on the Tires saddle (2440 m).

THE TRE CIME, 2999 m

The Tre Cime/Drei Zinnen are amongst the most famous peaks in the Alps. Situated in the Sexten Dolomites, they face Monte Cristallo to the west, Sorapis and the Marmarole mountains to the south-west and south, and the snow-clad Gailtaler Alps to the north-east. The Tre Cime have a central position in the Dolomiti di Sesto/Sextener Dolomiten Nature Park.

BEGUNJŠČICA, 2060 m

The Karavanke are interrupted by some important transit routes such as the Koren/Wurzenpass, Ljubelj/Loiblpass and Jezerski vrh/Seebergsattel. West of the Ljubelj/Loibl-pass is Begunjščica; eastwards the main ridge continues with the broad-shouldered Košuta/Koschuta massif (rising to 2133 m), the pointed Hochobir or Ojsterz (2139 m) and Peca/Petzen (2125 m) far in the distance.

GROSSVENEDIGER, 3667 m

Grossglockner's western neighbour in the Hohe Tauern is a real skier's mountain. From a bird's-eye perspective we can see that four rocky ridges meet at the summit, with four glaciers between them. The biggest, the Schlaten Glacier, descends eastward into the valley of the small Tauern Bach, which flows into the River Isel.

**MARMOLADA, 3343 m,
CIMON DELLA PALA, 3184 m**

Marmolada's south face is a long, rugged, 800-metre-high barrier with very demanding climbing routes. This view from the south-west, above the ski centre of San Martino di Castrozza and the surrounding ski slopes with lifts on the Rolle pass, also reveals the mighty face of Cimon della Pala.

HOCHALMSPITZE, 3360 m

Hochalmspitze, the queen of the Hohe Tauern, is the crowning peak of the Ankogel group. It is surrounded on all sides by glaciers, which are most extensive on the northern side – Grosselendkees and on the eastern side - Hochalmkees. The southern side has only the modest remains of the Trippkees glacier.

**KOČNA, 2475 m
GRINTOVEC, 2558 m**

The Kamnik-Savinja Alps are a range of two-thousanders with Grintovec having the highest altitude. The Alpine valleys of Robanov kot and Logarska dolina are protected as country parks, while documents are being prepared for the founding of the Kamnik-Savinja Alps Regional Park.

ŠKRLATICA, 2740 m

Škrlatica (the "scarlet" mountain) is the second highest peak in the Eastern Julian Alps and in Slovenia. The north-west faces of Škrlatica, Rakova špica and Rogljica take on a scarlet glow at sunset. The first to climb to the summit in 1880 was the "poet" of the Julian Alps, Dr. Julius Kugy, accompanied by Andrej Komac and Matija Kravanja, guides from the Trenta valley.

HOCHGALL / COLLALTO, 3436 m

This summit is on the Austrian-Italian border, at the meeting-point of the Riesenferner-Ahrn /Vedrette di Ries-Aurina Nature Park on the Italian side and the Hohe Tauern National Park on the Austrian. Hochgall is the highest mountain in the Defereggen group, which lies north of the Drau valley.

CIVETTA, 3220 m

The north-west face of Civetta, 1200 metres high and 3 km wide, is one of the biggest rock faces in the Alps. It was climbed in 1925 by the outstanding rope-team Solleder-Lettenbauer. In those times the ascent signified the most demanding climbing feat in the Alps.

TRIGLAV, 2864 m

Triglav, the highest summit of the Julian Alps and of Slovenia, has a symbolic role for the Slovenes, as it figures in the national coat-of-arms and in many logos of different associations. The Triglav National Park, the only national park in Slovenia, is also named after it. The first ascent of the mountain was made in 1778 by local climbers from Bohinj.

GROSSGLOCKNER, 3798 m

The south faces of Grossglockner with the superb Stüdlgrat ridge. The Hohe Tauern National Park is the largest protected region in the Alps and the second largest national park in Europe. The height difference between the lowest and highest points is 2600 m, which offers favourable conditions for a diversity of fauna and flora.

MALA BABA, 2018 m
OJSTRICA, 2350 m

Wonderful glacial valleys indent the Kamnik-Savinja Alps: Logarska dolina, Matkov kot and Robanov kot in the east, the Bela and Kamniška Bistrica valleys in the south, and Jezersko in the north. The north faces of Dolgi hrbet overshadow the single miniature glacier in these Alps, which is resisting global warming.

LAKE BLED

Lake Bled was formed in the glacial basin of the former Bohinj glacier. It is enhanced by a picturesque island with the baroque Church of the Virgin Mary. Traditional boats known as *pletne* are rowed to the island, taking visitors. Bled Castle stands atop the cliffs on the lake's northern shore.

THE KARAVANKE / KARAWANKEN

The Karavanke/Karawanken represent Slovenia's longest mountain range, extending 120 km from Tarvisio/Trbiž to Slovenj Gradec, with the highest summit being Stol/Hochstuhl (2236 m). They constitute the border between Austria and Slovenia. The northern faces are precipitous, whereas the southern side is characterized by high-altitude grassy slopes.

THE SECKAUER TAUERN

The softly rounded, grassy ridges of the Seckauer mountains form the eastern end of the Nieder Tauern, which drops gently down to the confluence of the Liesing and Mur rivers. The group acquired its name from the place Seckau in the Mur valley, which is well-known for its more than 800-year-old Benedictine monastery.

DÖSENTAL

East of Mallnitz in the Hohe Tauern National Park, the Dösental valley indents the Hochalmspitze massif. At the head of the valley somewhat above 2200 m lies Dösensee; this is the second biggest high-altitude lake in Carinthia.

THE GESÄUSE NATIONAL PARK

The Gesäuse National Park lies within the Ennstaler Alps in the Enns valley. The 150-year-old history of Austrian mountaineering lies written in the mighty north faces of Planspitze (2117 m), the highest peak Hochtor (2369 m) and the neighbouring summits. The park was founded in 2002. In the background are the Eisenerzer Alps and the Hochschwab range.

SCHLERN / SCILIAR, 2563 m

Schlern, the symbol of South Tyrol, rises in the Seiser Alm region. The dolomite towers of Santnerspitze (2413 m) and Euringerspitze (2394 m), which are cut off from the main massif, give the Schlern range a readily recognizable, indeed unique appearance.

MONTE PELMO, 3168 m
MONTE CIVETTA, 3220 m

Pelmo and Civetta are certainly among the best-known Dolomite peaks. Pelmo is a veritable throne, as it stands alone on a plateau between the Ampezzo, Cadore and Zoldo valleys. The Civetta group, which rises south-west of Pelmo, is separated from the Palle group by the Cordevole gorge. In the foreground is Croda da Lago.

THE ROSENGARTEN / CATINACCIO GROUP

This massif, which lies only 20 km east of Bolzano/Bozen between the valleys of Eisacktal and Val di Fassa, acquired its German name from the rosy mountains, which have a warm glow at sunset. The highest summit is Kesselkogel/ Catinaccio d'Antermoia (3004 m).

VAL DI FASSA

Val di Fassa, the valley of the River Avisio, is one of the biggest in the Dolomites. It is surrounded by the Rosengarten group to the west, Sassolungo and Sella to the north, Marmolada to the east and Pale to the south-east. The main economic activity is winter and summer tourism.

THE TOTES GEBIRGE

The mountains of the Totes Gebirge, the Limestone Alps, lie north-east of the Dachstein massif, west of the Ennstaler Alps and east of the Salzkammergut. The highest peaks are (left) Grosser Priel (2515 m) and Spitzmauer (2446 m). A barren, high-altitude karst plateau with numerous abysses extends towards the south.

THE DOLOMITES

Here a fantastic multitude of rocky pinnacles, crags, ridges and towers in the Western Julians merges with the Carnian Alps and the Dolomites, which descend southwards to the Po Plain. There is not a view to equal this anywhere else in the world.

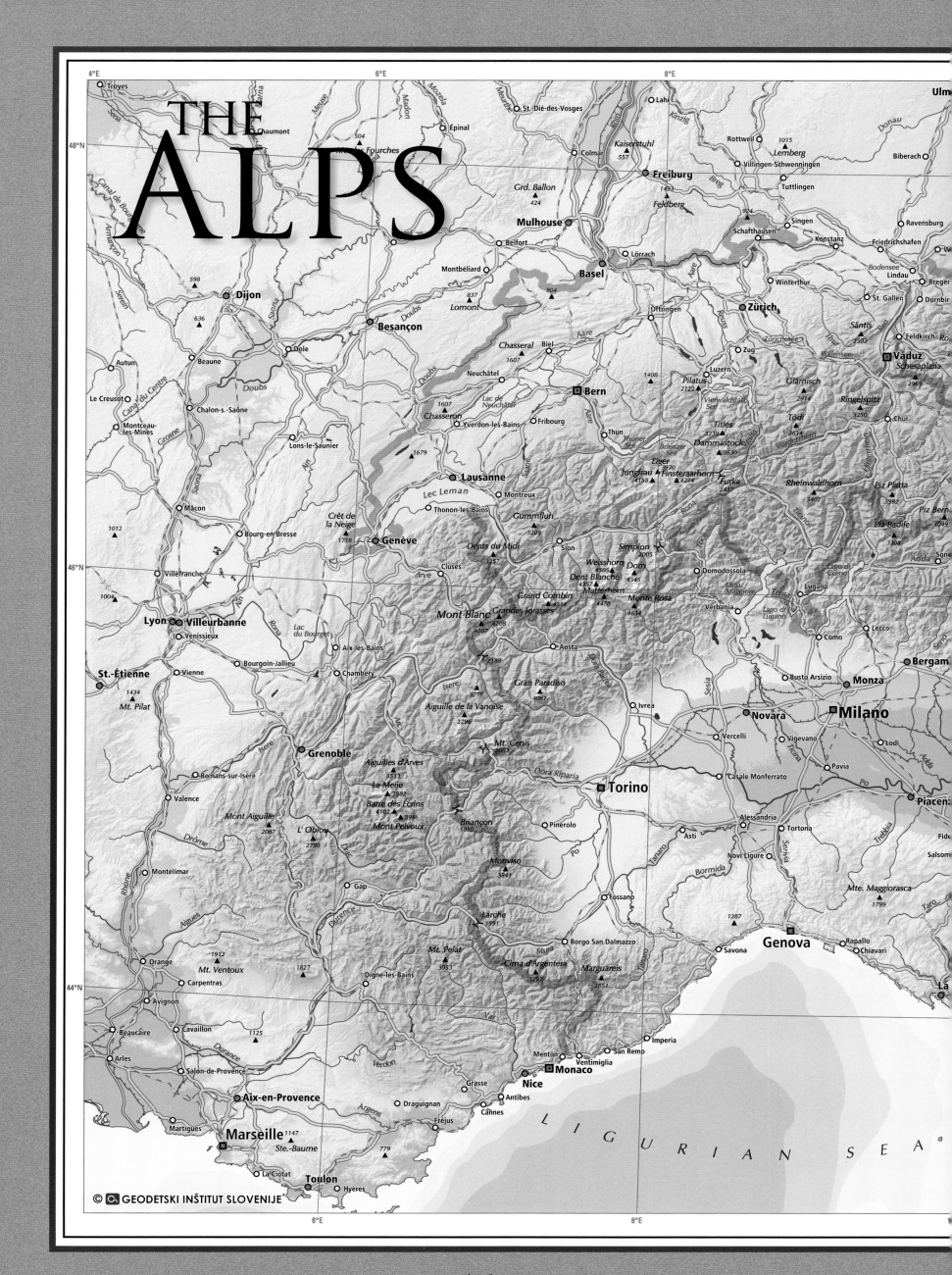

THE ALPS

Monte Chiavals [ITALY]

Uroš Herlec

THE GEOLOGY OF THE ALPS

The variety of rocks and of the geological structure of the Alps offers an insight into the history of how this region developed. The rocks were formed in different geological periods, varied environments and in changing climatic conditions. This was a response to the global tectonic and climatic happenings through a period of more than a billion years, the age of the oldest rocks. The evidence for the type and environment of rock formation and its metamorphosis as well as for the development of the Earth's surface in geological history enables us to understand the causes and effects of changes in the present natural environment.

Today's Alpine landscape is merely a short-lived image in terms of geological history. Apart from sudden "catastrophes" such as earthquakes, rockslides and avalanches, geological processes take place very slowly and in fact we are not aware of them. The relief has been formed over millions of years, changing all the time, and it will go on changing in the future as well. In the desire to understand how the Earth came into being, and how and why it changed and its surface is still changing, geologists study the composition and functioning of the planet – a gigantic machine, which is driven by the heat of the radioactive decay of the heavy elements in the Earth's core. Precisely the results of research studies in the Alps have explained many scientific questions and elucidated numerous geological processes. The most beautiful, most convincing and exemplary evidence of the geological processes that have shaped the territory of the Alps is the significant natural heritage. We all have a responsibility to preserve and protect this as a precious treasure, which has a unique scientific, educational and aesthetic value.

The Alps are an extensive European mountain chain over 1200 km long, stretching from France, across Germany, Liechtenstein, Switzerland and Italy to Austria and Slovenia. They are composed of rocks of the African and Eurasian tectonic plates. The Alps were formed through alpid orogenesis when the former Tethys Ocean was closed. Geologists link the beginning of the formation of each new mountain range with the formation of the rocks that compose it and with the processes of global tectonics that thrust up mountains.

Orogenesis, the process whereby mountain ranges are created, thus always begins with the breaking up of big supercontinents into smaller plates, opening up oceans between them. This results from the pressures of hot currents in the mantle rising to the Earth's crust and the settling of marine sediments. The Alps and the Himalayas are composed mostly of rocks that were formed in the one-time common Tethys Ocean. This started to open into the supercontinent of Pangaea at the beginning of the Triassic, about 250 million years ago. At the end of the middle Jurassic, the period of its greatest extent, it stretched from the present-day Caribbean via the Himalayas to the Burmese mountain arc. Global tectonic conditions started to change more quickly in the Jurassic, approximately 195 million years ago. At that time the central part of the Atlantic Ocean began to open up between modern North Africa and North America, while the Tethys Ocean began to close. At the end of the Jurassic the opening process happened most quickly in the southern Alantic, which caused the south-eastern part of Pangaea to start turning in an anti-clockwise direction, so closing the Tethys in its western part. In this process several smaller microplates on the edge of large plates broke off, while at the same time the ocean crust of The tethys began to be compressed and then subducted so that it sank beneath the European crust. When a large part of the ocean crust had already sunk in the lower Cretaceous, the first mountains were thrust up due to the first collision between continental microplates in the intermediate area between the African and Eurasian tectonic plates. The mountain ranges were uplifted as the continental plates approached one other, causing the ocean crust to sink, and as a result of the compressing, folding and rising of sediments laid down during millions of years of sedimentation on the ocean crust. As the mountains rose up, the rocks in the depths between the plates were metamorphized. The formation of the Alps in central Europe reached its climax about 15 million years ago and as a matter of fact has still not finished. To summarize: the uplifting of this mountain range resulted from the collision of the African and Eurasian tectonic plates and the extrusion of the sedimentary rocks laid down between them.

The convergence and fusion of the Eurasian and Adriatic microplates and the mutual overthrusting and subducting of parts of the upper and lower sections of one crust between the upper and lower sections of the other crust has been colourfully likened by researchers to a combat between two crocodiles. In a simplified way the geological structure of the Alps can be represented as the jaws of the two crocodiles clamped together. The upper jaw of each "crocodile" represents the upper, sedimental part of the continental crust, while the lower one represents its magmatic-metamorphic part.

The Adriatic "micro-crocodile" bit the upper jaw of the big Eurasian crocodile, but the latter paid it back by grabbing it by the lower jaw. The longest "thrust in" parts of the Adriatic microplate extend more than 200 km towards the north and cover the upper part of the Eurasian plate.

The sedimental rocks of the African plate – or the Adriatic microplate, as its former part – were thus thrust far to the north after the Eocenic collision with the Eurasian plate. In fact, the northern front of this overthrust extends to the southern margins of the Bavarian lowlands. This overthrust also includes the Austrian Northern Limestone Alps, which were pushed as a sedimental crust more than 200 km northwards over the Eurasian plate. The rocks of the Northern Limestone Alps were thus formed in the Tethys Ocean the same as the sediments of the Italian Dolomites and the Slovene Julian Alps, and geologically are the erstwhile edge of the African plate. In central Austria this "African" crust is mostly eroded, so that the substratum of metamorphic and sedimental rocks, which formed on the Eurasian tectonic plate, already appear on the surface from beneath the upper stratum of "African sediments" in the so-called erosion-tectonic windows of central Austria.

The ocean was closed by the slow movement and convergence of the plates. The closing of the ocean crust was followed by the thrusting of blocks of rocks, one over the other. The Insubrian and later Periadriatic fracture zone is famous, the most important fracture zone of the entire Alpine range, which is now no longer tectonically active. It represents the contact between the rocks of the Eurasian plate and the Adriatic microplate, which is a former part of a more extensive Africa. The fracture zone is a very deep transverse fault, along which there was extensive sliding between the tectonic plates. Because of the exceptional pressures, a considerable tectonic block of the Eurasian continent broke off and was pushed eastwards into the region between the present-day Pannonian plain and the Carpathians. The above-mentioned slide is evidenced by volcanic activity, with the formation of Oligocenic and Miocenic igneous rocks, tuffs and tufas.

The continued compression between the two plates in the Oligocene, 35 million years ago, with the anti-clockwise turning of the Adriatic plate, initiated the pushing out of the already partially subducted sections along a big fault, the so-called Periadriatic fault. In this process the overthrusting of sediments to the north and south of the fault continued.

In the Eocene and Oligocene the entire new mountain chain of the Alps was exposed to erosion. The rivers laid down at the foot of the mountains mechanical deposits from which clastic-mechanical sediments were formed: conglomerates, sandstones and silts. As the collision of the continents progressed, the crust continued to thicken, while the uplifting of the Alps and Dinarids confirmed the collision between the tectonic plates on the entire Alpine front. Meanwhile the heating of rocks in the depths was so intense that at temperatures above approximately 550°C certain minerals in the rocks in the substratum of the thickened crust melted and granodiorite magma began to form from them. Since this molten material was lighter than the surrounding rocks into which it forced its way, it rose along faults towards the surface

and thus contributed to the even faster uplifting of the new mountain range.

At the end of the Oligocene about 23 million years ago, the eastern part of the Alps again experienced powerful volcanic activity. This was caused by local stretching and opening deep into the Earth's crust along the steep Periadriatic fault, which borders the Adriatic microplate and the Eurasian plate. During this activity the major part of the Adriatic microplate moved more than 200 km eastwards. The section which prior to the anti-clockwise turning had been thrust about 200 km northwards onto the Eurasian plate remained there with it.

The subduction of the Eurasian plate beneath the Adriatic one gradually came to a halt from the Oligocene due to the ever greater quantities of less dense sediments. The continued convergence of the plates caused the rocks that had previously sunk between the two plates to be extruded, folded and extensively overthrust – a process that started about 20 million years ago and ended about 7 million years ago. North of the zone where the Alps were extruded, the rocks were thrust northwards, and south of the zone southwards. The two approaching tectonic plates pushed out and folded the rocks between them. Enormous folds were created. Continued compression caused them to break apart and the converging of the plates continued along gentle faults – overthrusts. Those that are pushed furthest and often cover younger rocks beneath them are termed covers. The overthrusting can be up to several hundred kilometres long.

The overthrust structure of the Alps thus came about through powerful pressures, extruding and folding the rocks between the two continental plates at the same time as they were uplifted. This overthrust and cover structure is one of the fundamental characteristics of the territory of the Alps. This means that when the Alps were created, rocks which had formed on a much more extensive territory were squeezed into the Alpine region.

As the Adriatic plate continued to turn, the tension brought about the youngest tectonic deformations in the Alps, fractures in a north-west–south-east direction. Precise geodetic measurements point to smaller sliding movements, a few millimetres per year in length, along some Dinaric fractures.

The opening up of the oceans and division of living space and the uplifting of mountain ranges also had an important influence on the development of life. In the past 65 million years animal and plant species have developed that have colonized complex ecosystems of today's world. In this process they had to adapt to climate changes which reached their peak in the Pleistocene ice ages. The biggest changes were caused by the cooling of the climate and the creation of the mountains. There was a warm and rainy period at the beginning of the Cenozoic and mammals were adapted to life in the forests, which covered the regions with sufficient rainfall. The movement of the continents, the uplifting of mountain ranges and climate changes influenced the variety of evolutionary routes in different parts of the world. With climate cooling, the weather took on a more seasonal character. This influenced forest vegetation and the diversity of ecological niches at different altitudes, which was followed by specialization in fauna and flora. Temperatures began to drop rapidly 38 million years ago. The climate on the whole Earth became drier, the forests retreated, and this was followed by several waves when species became extinct. In the Miocene the sea-level began to fall. An ever increasing amount of water was imprisoned in the growing ice sheets of the Antarctic and Greenland. At this time the alpine mountain chains of Europe, North and South America and Asia also rose quickly, which additionally contributed to the global cooling of the climate, followed by another wave of the extinction of species. Approximately 10 million years ago the face of the major part of the Earth's land surface changed, in that grasses developed. These could grow more or less permanently in places where other more demanding plants could not succeed. Their spread at the expense of forests fundamentally altered moderate and subtropical ecosystems.

In the Pleistocene period in the last 1.8 million years extensive parts of the land surface in extreme geographical latitudes have often been covered by glaciers. The analysis of marine sediments showed that there were more than 20 main glacial periods. Previously, on the basis of the glacial sediments, only six ice ages had been presumed – glacials with intervening warmer periods – interglacials. In some of these interglacial periods, when the glaciers retreated, the climate was warmer than it is today. At present we are in one of the interglacial periods, when the extent of glacier cover is rapidly decreasing.

The tectonic forces that have created the present-day territory of Slovenia are still active now. The frequent earthquakes warn us that the African and Eurasian plates continue to converge, so that the Slovene mountains are still rising. Most of the world's earthquakes occur precisely on the borders of tectonic plates. The majority are found in subduction zones and zones where continental plates collide. Earthquakes result from the fracturing of rocks and sudden movements of blocks of rocks beside the fractures whenever the tension, which gradually builds up beside harder or rougher parts that impede their movement, is released very quickly. Such tensions accumulate up to the point when they exceed the friction between blocks of rocks. Then there is movement and a new earthquake happens. Their frequency in Slovenia indicates the great tensions in the rocks deep below the surface.

Jungfrau glacier [SWITZERLAND]

Michael Zemp

GLACIER CHANGES
IN THE ALPS

In the densely populated European Alps, glaciers are an inherent component of the landscape, environment and culture. They represent a unique source of freshwater for agricultural, industrial and domestic use, an important economic component of tourism and hydroelectric power production, but are also a source of serious natural hazards. Our glaciers generally form where the winter snow is not entirely melted by the summer's strong insolation and warm temperatures. Because the Alpine ice is close to the melting point, glaciers react strongly to climate change, and thereby provide some of the clearest evidence for it.

Many of us remember the snowy winters of the 1970s and early 1980s, when winter sport activities were possible over many weeks even in the lowlands, and many glaciers, such as the Argentière (F), Oberer Grindelwald (CH), Pre de Bar (I) or Waxegg (A), pushed their icy tongues down-valley – what a different sight to the ice wasting away at present! However, how many still remember the strong glacier retreats of the 1940s, or the advances of the 1920s? Scientists have been systematically collecting information on glacier changes and carrying out regular measurements of glacier length changes since the 19th century. These early measurements together with dated moraines representing glacier maximum extents of past times, a complete inventory of all the Alpine glaciers compiled on the basis of maps and aerial photographs of the 1970s, annual glacier mass balance measurements – the annual thickness change of a glacier averaged over the glacier area – since the late 1940s, and numerous computer modelling studies provide us with a detailed picture of past, present and potential future glacier changes in the Alps.

During the maximum extent of the last Ice Age, 20,000 to 25,000 years ago, Alpine glaciers covered an area of about 150,000 km². In the north the glacier tongues reached down to the pre-Alpine lowlands, in the south they advanced to the margin of the Padan Plain (in the Po Valley). In Zurich, for example, about 15 km upstream/up-glacier from the maxi-mum front position, the Linth Glacier was still about 300 m thick. After this glacial maximum, Alpine glaciers

started to retreat gradually with typical patterns of staggered sequences of moraines that testify to intermittent periods of glacier re-advances during the overall retreat. The moraines of the Younger Dryas (i.e., the period of 12,600-11,500 years ago) are a conspicuous feature in many valleys and mark the last major re-advance of the Late Glacial period. After that last major re-advance, glaciers reached similar extents to those of today at the beginning of the Holocene (i.e., the period of the last 10,000 years). During the Holocene, glacier front variations fluctuated within relatively narrow margins as compared to the Late Glacial changes. Dated stumps of trees and peat as well as archaeological finds such as Ötzi, the 5300-year-old Iceman found on the Austrian-Italian border, document periods of reduced and expanded glacier states during that time. Periods of reduced glacier states were found during the Bronze Age (about 3800-2800 years ago), at the transition from the Iron Age (about 2800-2450 years ago) to the Roman Age (about 2450-1600 years ago), and during the Middle Ages (about 1500-500 years ago); major glacier advances took place around 3000-2600, 1500-1400, 1200-1100, and 900-800 years ago, as well as during the Little Ice Age (700-140 years ago).

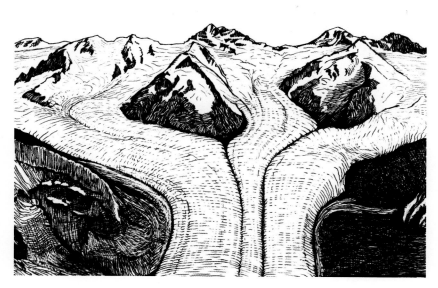

The Aletsch Glacier

The moraines of the last Little Ice Age advance, around 1850, mark Holocene maximum glacier extents in the Alps. From these positions, glaciers have shown an overall dramatic retreat until the present day. Large valley glaciers such as the Grosser Aletsch (CH), Morteratsch (CH) or Pasterze (A) have retreated continuously, whereas mid-sized and steeper glaciers have reacted to somewhat wetter and cooler periods with intermittent re-advances in the 1890s, 1920s, and 1970-80s.

A complete inventory of the Alpine glaciers was made in the 1970s. 5150 glaciers were identified with a total area of 2900 km²; 90% of the glaciers were smaller than 1 km² and together covered about one third of the total area; the largest seven glaciers make up one tenth of the total ice cover. Overall, the Alpine glacier cover is calculated to have diminished by about 35% from 1850 to the 1970s and by another 22% up to 2000. The corresponding loss in ice volume is estimated as 50% and 25% respectively. Mass balance observations over the past six decades reveal large ice losses in the first two decades, close to steady-state conditions between the mid 1960s and mid 1980s, followed by a fast and accelerated ice loss up to the present. According to these measurements, glaciers have thinned by more than 20 m over the past 25 years, with an annual average ice loss of more than one metre of ice per year since the turn of the century.

The onset of glacier retreat from their Little Ice Age moraines and the intermittent re-advances might at least partly be attributed to periods of increased snow accumulation. However, the main cause of the dramatic retreat of the Alpine glaciers over the past 150 years is to be found in the human-induced temperature increase. Alpine temperatures have increased by about 1.5°C over the past 150 years – about twice as much as on the global average. In the same time half of the Alpine ice cover has been lost. According to the current state-of-the-art climate scenarios, we are facing a potential additional temperature increase of 1 to 6 °C by the end of the 21st century, depending on which of the plausible greenhouse gas emission scenarios is applied. Under such conditions we must expect a dramatic continuation of present glacier wasting. Glaciers will retreat well beyond their margins of the Holocene and the present day. In fact they would only be able to survive on some of the highest Alpine peaks, with impacts on our landscape, hydrological cycle and natural hazard potential that are beyond any historical analogy.

Some facts and figures:

Number of glaciers (1970s): 5150

Estimated glacier cover:
around 1850: 4400 km², 200 km³
around 1970: 2900 km², 100 km³
around 2000: 2200 km², 75 km³

The largest Alpine glaciers

#	Name	Country	Year	Area (km²)	Length (km)
1	Grosser Aletsch	CH	1973	86.8	24.7
2	Gorner	CH	1973	68.9	14.1
3	Fiescher	CH	1973	33.1	16.0
4	Mer de Glace	F	1967	33.1	12.3
5	Unteraar	CH	1973	28.4	13.5
6	Oberaletsch	CH	1973	21.7	9.1
7	Unterer Grindelwald	CH	1973	21.7	9.0
8	Pasterze	A	1969	19.8	9.2
23	Forni	I	1981	13.2	5.5
....	Schneeferner Nord	D	1975	0.4	0.9

Source: Data from the World Glacier Inventory, hosted at the World Glacier Monitoring Service (www.wgms.ch).

Tschierva glacier - Bernina [SWITZERLAND]

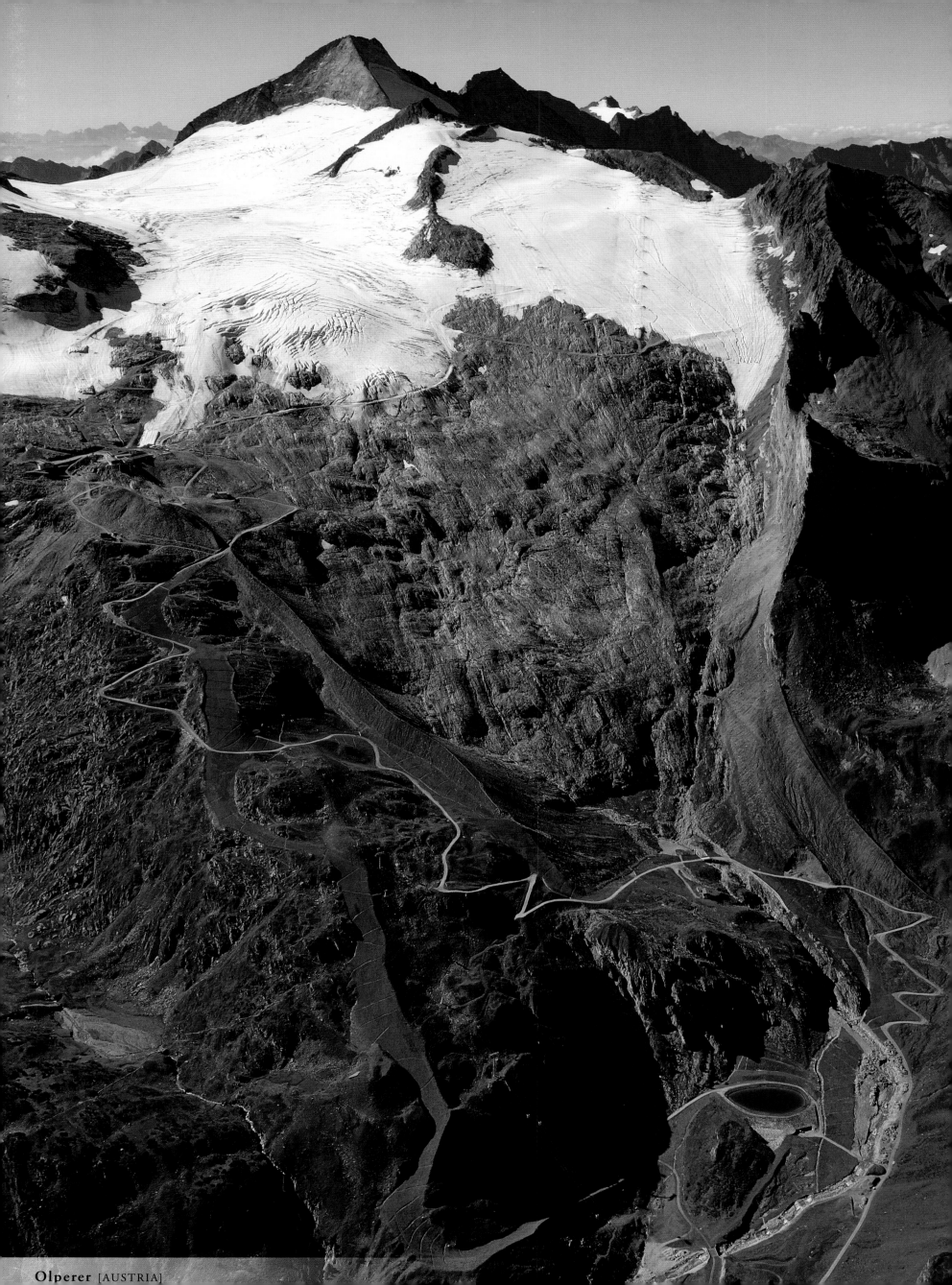

Olperer [AUSTRIA]

Lučka Kajfež Bogataj

THE CLIMATE OF THE ALPS AND EXPECTED CHANGES

The Alps cover a broad swathe of Europe, since they are about 200 km wide and over 1200 km long. The highest summits reach from 4500-4800 m. Although the Alps are not extensive in the north-south direction and thus do not experience great differences in solar radiation, the climate of the Alps is very varied and changeable, due to their position between the Atlantic Ocean, the Mediterranean Sea and continental Europe. The climate is shaped by the functioning of weather systems which form and spread above the Alps from over the northern Atlantic, the Mediterranean and Eurasia. The Alps through their location have a decisive influence on the movement of cyclones, which arise above the Atlantic and move eastwards, themselves influencing the formation of secondary cyclones, such as the Genoan, which arise above the Gulf of Genoa. With their situation and noticeably diverse topography, these mountains influence the formation of strong winds and extremely variable weather conditions locally.

THE CLIMATE OF THE ALPS, AS WE KNOW IT TODAY

In summer the weather is generally warm and sunny in lower valleys and pleasantly cool at higher altitudes. In winter the valleys are often colder, since the colder air creeps down the mountainsides and gathers like a sea in the valleys and especially in basins. The Alps are frequently dominated in winter by an area of high pressure, which causes temperature inversion, thus cold and foggy air is trapped beneath warm air.

The climate in the Alps changes noticeably with location. The heaviest precipitation falls in the south-eastern Alps, i.e. the Julian and Carnian Alps. Brought by damp winds from the Adriatic and northern Mediterranean, up to 4000 mm of precipitation annually can fall in these regions, whereas the remaining Alps receive from 1200 to 1600 mm per year. On the southern side of the Alps most precipitation falls in winter, under the influence of the Mediterranean, while on the northern side of the Alps most falls in summer. The Alpine climate is also characterized by great differences in daytime temperatures.

The depth of the snow cover in the mountains and the altitude of the tree-line depend on the gradient of mountain slopes and their exposure to sunshine and warm air currents. The tree-line occurs at an altitude where the average July temperature is approximately 10°C. In the Slovene Alps it is around 1700 metres high, while in the Central Alps it can rise to as much as 2400 metres. The boundary of permanent snow and ice is difficult to determine. The occurrence of meterological conditions that are favourable for snow (i.e. colder and damper) in successive seasons lowers it. The lower snow boundary is about 800 m higher than the tree-line; in some parts of the Alps the former lies about 2400 m high, while elsewhere it cannot fall below 3300 m on account of relief features.

In those regions of the Alps that drop down towards the northern Mediterranean there is abundant vegetation. Typical Mediterranean bushes and olive trees are found in sheltered places at the foot of the mountains, and olive trees also grow in quite deep valleys and on the shores of many Italian lakes which penetrate into the Alps. Vines are tolerant of low temperatures; they grow successfully even deeper in the valleys of the Alps and also towards the interior of this extensive mountain chain, especially on sunny slopes.

THE CLIMATE IS CHANGING

The last fifteen years in the Alps have been amongst the warmest in the last 500 years. Cold and snowy winters here are increasingly rare while the summers are becoming drier, and disasters caused by the weather more common. Actually, the climate has changed many times in the last three million years and for a variety of reasons: the radiation and movement of the Sun has changed and the movement of the Earth, there have been surface changes on land and sea, mountain ranges have arisen, the ice cover on land and sea has altered, and so on. Very strong climatic changes can be provoked by altered properties of the atmosphere, which influence the exchange of energy between the Earth and the universe. When the energy of solar radiation received is no longer the same as the

Lake Dvojno jezero [SLOVENIA]

Anton Brancelj

ALPINE WATERS

Just a quick glance at a map of the Alps shows that they are an important source of water. The highest regions on the map are white because of the presence of glaciers. This is also confirmed by the view of Earth from space. The Alpine landscape is marked by a series of big lakes situated on the margin of the Alps massif, where the mountains give way to plains. There are at least 40 with a surface area exceeding 10 km² and which lie only 200, 300 or 500 m above sea-level. The lowest, at merely 65 m above sea-level, is Lago di Garda. All the lakes are elongated in shape, which points to the important role played by glaciers in their formation. During the ice ages the glaciers slid from higher positions into the valleys, which were mostly determined by geological faults caused by the uplifting of the Alps. These faults were deepened and widened by the glaciers. Thus many Alpine lakes are several tens of metres deep, some even more than 100 m. The four deepest are even deeper than 300 m, these being Lago di Como – 425 m; Lago Maggiore – 370 m; Lago di Garda – 350 m; Lac Léman (also called Lake Geneva) – 310 m. The surface area of some lakes exceeds 200 km² : Lac Léman – 581 km², Bodensee (also called Lake Constance) – 571 km², Lago di Garda – 368 km², Lac de Neuchâtel – 218 km², Lago Maggiore – 213 km². The depth and surface area of the lakes are also expressed in the volume of water, which is measured in tens of cubic kilometres: Lac Léman – 89 km³, Bodensee – 55 km³, Lago di Garda – 49 km³, Lago Maggiore – 38 km³, Lago di Como – 23 km³. All these lakes at the foot of the Alps represent a huge supply of drinking water for the surrounding as well as more distant inhabitants.

In the past there was plenty of cargo and passenger traffic along the big lakes, linked with the fairly dense settlement of the area. Nowadays these lakes are becoming increasingly important from the tourist standpoint as well, since an ever greater number of people decide to spend part of their holidays on the lake shores. These factors – dense settlement, industry, traffic and tourism – now represent a serious threat to the shores and the water of these lakes, seen in the diminished water quality, which leads to rising costs and bigger efforts for preservation.

In addition to the big lakes, there are a multitude of smaller Alpine lakes, whose number runs into the hundreds. They are found from the foothills right up to the foot of glaciers, a region dominated by permanent snow and ice. In terms of their surface area and depth they are less impressive than the lakes in the valleys, but they give a special character to the landscape. People have a special attitude towards lakes above the tree-line, as they are considered a symbol of pure, unspoilt nature. These smaller lakes were also formed by the action of glaciers in the past. All the Alpine lakes are relatively young, since they appeared only after the retreat or melting of glaciers, i.e. 8000-10,000 years ago, when hollow depressions were filled with water. Due to their small size and higher altitude, different conditions obtain in mountain lakes than in the big lakes below the Alps. Unlike the lowland lakes, which in winter are only exceptionally completely covered in ice, most mountain lakes are covered for at least half the year by a layer of ice up to one metre thick. There can also be some metres of snow on top of the ice, which additionally pushes their liberation from the ice cover far into the spring or early summer. The long-lasting ice cover and high altitude means that the water in mountain lakes is cold even in the summer. Above 2000 m the temperature of the surface water only rarely rises above 10-12°C. And just one or two metres below the surface the temperature is only 4°C or even a degree colder all year round. But this is sufficient so that the lakes do not freeze completely in the winter. The only exceptions are the shallowest lakes. Water (i.e. in its liquid state) enables tiny plants and animals to survive the seemingly unfavourable winter conditions. Also lakes high in the mountains, even above 2500 m, offer a habitat to some truly scarce yet resilient plant and animal species. These are mostly microscopic algae, which live in the water (plant plankton) or cover stones on the lake bottom. The animals are represented by tiny crustaceans from the copepod and water-flea groups, 1-2 mm in size, and often bright red in colour. They live either in the water or among stones on the lake bed, where the larvae of some water insects are found. Lower down towards the valley the number of plant and animal species increases. Near the tree-

Verdon [FRANCE]

Boštjan Anko

ALPINE FORESTS

As an ecological system, a forest is the most developed living community on land. In normal conditions it is characterized by a great amount of organic material, which is richly structured (living, dead, above or below ground), slowly rotates, yet is permanently present, all of which ensures an exceptional biodiversity of flora, fungi and fauna. In its essence a forest is a community of relative abundance, which its members share out by means of countless strategies. In the mountains a clear division can be observed between vegetation zones, passing from the lowlands through hills to foothills and then to the mountains with their montane, subalpine, and finally alpine zones; the last mentioned having no trees at all. Each of these zones is marked by particular conditions (influenced primarily by climate) for successful forest growth – and appropriately different plant and animal associations for a forest environment. It is said that on the way towards mountain summits, with every 100 metres of altitude gained, the conditions for plant life change as much as if they had moved 150 kilometres further north. The intensification of living conditions in the mountains is seen especially in the ever harsher climate: lower temperatures, great temperature extremes, winds, ever shorter vegetative periods when organisms need to create reserves for the cold part of the year. Whenever and wherever conditions for the survival of individual "interest groups" become more difficult, strategies of mutual competition are joined quite noticeably by basic survival strategies. Organisms capable of adapting to more demanding conditions begin to replace those which cannot do this. The crew changes, the boat-forest remains.

Mountain forests are exposed to avalanches, rockslides, rolling boulders and falling stones, etc., which directly destroy their stands or literally push them down the hillsides.

The lurking danger embodied in all these factors is largely dependent not only on the altitude, but also on the relief, which in comparison with the situation of valley forests changes with minute variations, especially where gradient and exposure are concerned. Of course, the structure and functioning of the forest also change accordingly.

The range of tree species which survive in such conditions is dramatically reduced. As the extremity and variation of the habitats increase, so the trees combine more and more into groups, to make the best possible use of better habitat conditions, so as to ensure mutual mechanical stability and a microclimate which is utilized by other organisms, especially their own new stock, which germinates in the shelter they provide.

The vegetative periods on the tree-line last about three months. With every 100 metres of altitude, these are additionally shortened by about a week. The growth periods in the valleys can be practically twice as long. The difference is obvious: the production of plant organic matter in an Alpine forest is essentially lower. Outwardly this is expressed in the denser annual rings of smaller and more stocky trees, which are more resistant to the unfavourable influences of the environment. Their root systems are more strongly developed, but the stands are thinner: each sunbeam is precious for photosynthesis.

For all these reasons the stocks of organic matter in an Alpine forest are considerably smaller than in forests at lower altitudes. Their decomposition is also slower.

Another characteristic that stands out in the structure of Alpine forests is that of age difference. That is, two neighbouring and apparently similar trees of the same species can differ in age by one or two centuries. One has germinated in shallow soil, and the other a century later in a richer pocket of soil.

In more favourable conditions, which are found in most managed forests, a stand can be regenerated in five to ten years. In an Alpine forest at high altitudes the regeneration period can last a century or one and a half centuries. Thus the differences in age there between descendants surrounding the same parent tree are measured according to human generations.

With such a slow tempo of life in Alpine forests, people therefore often did not know – or do not know – how to adapt their demands to what the forest can achieve in a given period of time.

In human terms, slow caution, incredible patience and even more incredible persistence are the main strategies of Alpine forests in the struggle for survival. They are adapted to the slow rhythm dictated by an environment that is less and less friendly to life. Wherever and whenever people did not understand this, the forest suffered first, and then in some way or other people themselves.

A deeper insight into the structure and functioning of living communities in the Alps is also provided by data on the variety of life forms within them. The concept of biodiversity is by no means simple: often it is not clear whether it is the diversity of life forms from some past age, diversity which would come about without human intervention – or precisely because of it, and then, of course, diversity on the genetic, species, ecosystem or landscape levels. All these aspects of biodiversity are in general insufficiently studied, and this is especially the case in the Alps.

Nevertheless, it is interesting that the Alps – at least as far as plant life is concerned - constitute one of the most bountiful regions in Europe. As much as 40% of European flora can be found here. Due to the geographical isolation, tectonic uplifting, varied climatic changes that depend on altitude and exposure, the history of glacial periods, great differences in the formation of microhabitats, the different history of the migrations and development of species, as well as human influences, the biodiversity in the Alps is exceptional.

On a big time and space scale we must take into account the fact that during the alternating glacial and warm periods, the Alps with their west-east axis always represented a barrier to species which retreated to the south in front of the ice or followed it towards the north whenever it retreated. In refuges not affected by glaciation, many plant and animal species were preserved. Similarly, about 400 endemic plant species have been preserved in the Alps.

On a small time and space scale – e.g. just a few square metres and one vegetational period – the biodiversity of the Alps is influenced by the endless variation of the relief, linked with microclimatic differences. The southern side of a boulder has a completely different microclimate than the northern side – and of course different inhabitants. It is the same with the northern and southern slopes of a steeply carved out Alpine valley.

The degree to which the natural biodiversity in the Alps is preserved or changed alongside all these factors depends on the history of human influences (their beginning, intensity, duration, cessation, etc.). This also holds true for Alpine forests: whereas in more easily accessible forests, man often laid a heavy hand (with harsh consequences) and introduced questionable plantings as regards species and genetics in the clearings, in the Alps extensive areas of literally virgin forests were still preserved with evolutionarily selected communities of living creatures. Here it is clear why precisely because of the history of glacial periods, the composition of tree species is more varied in some places or why a living forest community on the shady side of one mountain will always be different from that on its sunny side.

By introducing economically interesting tree species of unsuitable provenance, people in the Alps made big mistakes. But in virgin forests it is still possible to find centuries-old warrior trees, frequently wounded yet still victorious, which carry in their genetic records the secret of survival in an unfriendly environment, and pass it down to their progeny. Their stories are the narrative of the Alpine forest.

One of the most dramatic boundaries in nature is the tree-line. With all its diversity it can be compared with the coastline, where land and ocean meet.

When conditions are no longer suitable for trees to grow, they as the predominant life form soon give way to increasingly dwarf growth forms. In the Alps the tree-line can reach as high as 2300 metres, but generally it coincides with positions where the vegetation period lasts at least three months, while the average monthly temperature of the warmest month is at least 10°C.

In the past people lowered the Alpine tree-line in many places by 200-400 metres, especially with pasturage.

Above the line of compact forest there is often a transitional zone stretching up a few hundred metres, where in more favourable conditions as regards microclimate, soil and relief just some individual trees defy all the probabilities. In scientific language this is the subalpine zone, but the frequently used expression "battle zone" (Kampfzone) more clearly describes its essence. Its upper boundary represents the so-called upper tree-line. Approximately 27,000 km² of the Alps extend above this.

The usual presentations of forests give details of their surface area, timber stocks, annual growth, etc. But exact data of this kind are not available for Alpine forests since appropriate criteria are not unified among the Alpine countries – or the data simply do not exist. In most national forest inventories, Alpine forests form just a part of all the forests in a particular country. Thus we can only mention estimates, which assume 7.5 million hectares of forests in the Alps, which is supposed to represent 43% forest cover. 80-90% of these forests are considered profitable, while the remainder is shown in official surveys as "unprofitable". The timber stock in managed forests is valued at 1.5 billion m³ , while average timber stocks in individual countries vary from 160 to 360 m³. The annual increment is estimated at 37 million m³. The number of trees is thought to exceed 3 billion, which reckoned against 11 million inhabitants of the Alps would mean 270 trees per person. And so on.

What essential information about Alpine forests can these number games give us? Nothing – except that at the beginning of the 21st century, the countries considered to be among the richest look upon forest, also in extreme conditions, as primarily a stack of timber and that forests in which felling is not possible are no longer "profitable" in their eyes.

Certainly timber has long been a very important renewable raw material, but a forest is more than just timber. Its services – environmental and social – in a wealthy yet tired world are becoming ever more significant.

The Alps are often called the "water tower of Europe". They intercept enormous quantities of precipitation, which without the alleviating impact of the forest cover would surge in torrents into the valleys together with all their alluvia.

It has been known for centuries that the Alpine forest gives significant protection against erosion, but the Alpine countries still do not have a unified definition for such protective forest, let alone unified strategies for dealing with it. The Alpine forest also mitigates climatic extremes, absorbs CO_2, constitutes a genetic treasury, provides space for recreation, and is a source of beauty, peace and inspiration.

What kind of future does the Alpine forest have? Uncertain, stormy. This was declared in a sort of symbolic way by the Vivian (February 1990) and Lothar (December 1999) storms. Tens of millions of cubic metres of wood fell in three days. Huge gaps appeared in Alpine forests.

With the changes in temperature, which are emphasized still more in the Alps, we can only expect the tree-line to move higher. The future of the Alpine forests will also be affected by pollution and changes in the human pressures on them. Probably the most interesting chapter in the future of the Alps and of Alpine forests concerns the shift in man's attitude towards them. Seemingly, man has so far fought against the Alps and perhaps in the future will fight for the Alps. From Hannibal up to today's traffic corridors, the Alps have been above all a big obstacle to a wide swathe of Europe. The Alpine countries have chopped them centrifugally, while for the rest of Europe (and still further afield) they were just a vast area for recreation.

The view of the Alps as a whole derives from the period in the mid 20th century when a new Europe came into being. Was it only after the war that people realized the Alps have their own identity, a certain intrinsic value, which they did not appreciate so long as they lived in their own valleys and within their own borders? That it was not just people that left their stamp on the Alps, but also the other way round? Clearly the forests with their natural, social and economic importance played a significant role in this.

Documents such as the Convention on the Protection of the Alps (1991) with the protocol Mountain Forest, the Schaan Memorandum (2006) or the Resolution on Wilderness Areas (2007) represent just a few steps in the new direction. They are full of hope but also of uncertainty, because they drag behind them a century-old burden of indifference towards those parts of the Alps and those forests which are "no longer of use". What use? Does an environmental service count as a use? Does a wilderness area, a national park or Natura 2000 count as a use? Does a walk through the forest count as a use? Doesn't satisfying the desire for peace, biodiversity or beauty count as a use?

It is a pity that the old stereotypes about the Alps and their nature melt away more slowly than the Alpine glaciers …

Triglav [SLOVENIA]

Tone Wraber

ALPINE FLORA

Alpine flora is attractive not only because of its special characteristics but also because experiencing it is closely linked with experiencing the Alpine world, its nature and people. This chapter will deal only with Alpine flora.

Under the title Alpine flora we generally think of the plant world above the tree-line, i.e. in the region where trees can no longer grow, but the Alps begin on the plains and their ridges and summits are separated by more or less deep valleys. So Alpine flora also includes plants which grow only at lower altitudes, such as hop hornbeam (*Ostrya carpinifolia*) and holm oak (*Quercus ilex*), and differ in many points from plants that inhabit the region of the highest peaks. This brings us to the division of Alpine flora according to altitude, which is more obvious, at least from a distance, than the horizontal one, which gives rise, for example, to the Eastern and Western Alps distinction between plants. The geological substrate, which with the differing chemical and physical properties of the soil greatly influences the extent and variety of the plant world, is extremely important. The distribution of plants can differ in the same areas with the same geological conditions – due to the difference between sunny and shady exposure. Alpine flora can also be greatly influenced by the vegetation of its geographical surroundings, which is clearly seen in the presence of plants introduced into the Alps that do not occur in other Alpine areas. Although the Alps are a geographically unified region, their plant history has been varied, differing for instance in the north, which was more exposed to the influence of glaciation periods than the south was. All these factors appear in endemism, i.e. the presence of regionally different plants which do not occur elsewhere. In connection with Alpine flora it is worth bearing in mind the cultural element, that is, knowledge of the history of man's exploration of the Alpine world, often carried out precisely with a naturalist's curiosity. We can also consider human action that has an unfavourable influence on Alpine nature, and the conservation of nature, which aims to remove or at least reduce these influences.

Since 2004 we have had the long awaited work, *Flora alpina*, a professionally compiled and executed international project by four main Swiss authors (Aeschimann et al.). It presents all the known species of this most outstanding European mountain range, each with its scientific name and more common synonyms, as well as its names in the languages of the Alpine nations, with the family it belongs to, data on its life span, form, height, flowering period, distribution, type of habitat, phytocenological type, altitude range, type of substrate and habitat (moisture, reaction and nutrient value of the soil), with a photograph and map of its distribution in 55 administrative units within the Alpine countries. This book presents 4491 Alpine species, of which 501 are endemic. It is interesting for comparison that *Flora Europaea* (1964-1980) quotes 11,557 species for the territory of Europe. But in both cases it must be remembered that knowledge of the systematics of European and thus Alpine plants is by no means complete. More than on the detailed investigation of territory (for which after some centuries the facts are more or less established), knowledge depends on the differing theoretical approaches to research and thus is subject to each stage of development in this science. The truth of this is illustrated by the example of endemic genera. There are supposed to be three endemic genera in the Alps, of which each has just one species. These are the monotypic genera *Berardia*, *Physoplexis*

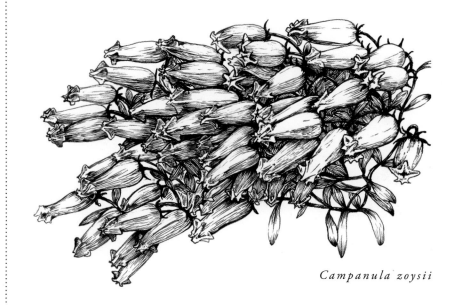

Campanula zoysii

and *Rhizobotrya*, to which could be added a fourth, *Hladnikia*, also with just one species, which is from the Trnovski gozd forest, near the Alps. In recent times a view over a century old has been renewed that the endemic species *Campanula zoysii* (Zois bellflower) of the South-East Limestone Alps belongs to the independent genus of *Favratia*. Strictly speaking, the Zois bellflower, found predominantly in Slovenia and its Friulian-Carinthian neighbourhood, is not an endemic species, since it also grows in the Trnovski gozd, which is the north-western part of the Dinaric mountain system; here the *Hladnikia pastinacifolia*, referred to above, also grows. There is no endemic family in the Alps, but some genera, including *Saxifraga*, *Festuca*, *Campanula*, *Gentiana* and *Primula*, have a considerable proportion of endemic species. Out of the 4491 species of Alpine flora, 3482 are native, but extending outside the Alps as well, 417 are strictly endemic (only in the Alps), 24 are probably endemic, 60 are subendemic (predominantly occurring in the Alps), 454 are adventive and 54 probably adventive species.

Endemism viewed on a world scale does not figure particularly high in Europe, but after the Mediterranean, it is highest in the Alps. Here and in the Carpathian mountains comparative research was carried out by the Polish botanist Bogumił Pawłowski (1970), who established that the number of Alpine endemites is highest in the Maritime Alps. They include, e.g. the endemic monotypic genus *Berardia subacaulis* from the Daisy family and the wonderful *Saxifraga florulenta*.

Saxifraga florulenta

Then follow the Eastern Alps with the region between Lake Como and Monte Baldo (e.g. several species of the genera *Moehringia* and *Saxifraga*), the Dolomites (the generic endemite *Rhizobotrya alpina*), the South-East Limestone Alps (the Carnian, Julian and Kamnik Alps, the Karavanke) (e.g. the generic endemite *Favratia zoysii*, *Moehringia villosa*, *Cerastium julicum*, *Gentiana froelichii* subsp. *froelichii* and subsp. *zenariae*, *Helictotrichon petzense*) and the North-East Limestone Alps (e.g. *Dianthus alpinus* and several species of the montane zone on the Lower Austrian edge of the Alps). The abundance of endemic species in these regions is connected with their geographical position. They are areas which in the Pleistocene were not covered with ice or not completely, or were then close to such areas, so that their local flora could be preserved. Plants were also able to survive in ice-free "oases" (termed *nunataks* in the Eskimo language) within otherwise ice-covered territory. Ice-free regions mostly occurred on the southern, western and eastern margins of the Alps, e.g. on the Lower Austrian Alps margin in the montane zone, while in the South-East Limestone Alps in some of the higher zones. There is an interesting occurrence of pairs where one species (or subspecies) grows in the South-East and the other in the North-East Limestone Alps: *Minuartia cherlerioides* subsp. *cherlerioides-M. ch.* subsp. *quadrifaria*, *Soldanella minina-S. austriaca*, *Heracleum austriacum* subsp. *siifolium-H. a.* subsp. *austriacum*, *Leucanthemum lithopolitanicum-L. atratum*, etc. These basophilic plants with an exclusive habitat appeared after the compact distribution of an original species was interrupted in the geological past; this was caused by the loss of the carbonate substrate removed in the Central Alps.

The geological substrate is generally an important factor in floral diversity. The first one to point this out was the physician and naturalist B. Hacquet, who in 1779 observed the difference between the plant life of the carbonate Alps in Carniola and the non-carbonate Hohe Tauern in Carinthia. This contrast is very noticeable in the vegetation cover, since plant associations which differ in species but are physiognomically similar appear on both substrates. A classic example of this is grassland communities of *Caricetum firmae* s. lat. on a carbonate substrate and of *Caricetum curvulae* s. lat. on a silicate substrate; there are numerous other such examples. The characteristic form of the names of plant associations should remind us that at the beginning of the 20th century the Alps were the starting-point for what is now the most established method of studying plant associations, i.e. phytocenology.

Naturally, Alpine vegetation is also greatly influenced by climatic differences. This is clearly seen in the altitude of the tree-line and the tree species constituting it, beech in the wettest (oceanic) regions, spruce and Swiss pine in more continental regions; it is slightly less obvious in the species composition, which influences the general appearance of the landscape. The wettest part of the Alps is in the south-east (the Julian Alps), while in the dry valleys of the interior, e.g. the Aosta valley in Italy, the Lower Engadine in Switzerland and the Möll valley in Austria, real steppe vegetation is found.

Everyone knows that vegetation changes with increasing altitude. Thus a number of altitude zones are distinguished, beginning with a hill zone, which then passes into the montane, subalpine, alpine and nival zones. Forests end at the tree-line on the upper boundary of the montane zone. This boundary fluctuates in altitude depending on the size of the mountain range, the climatic conditions and geological substrate, while human activity is a secondary factor. Higher up, non-forest vegetation is developed, which covers scrubland, Alpine heath, snow patches, grasslands, rocks and screes, becoming ever scarcer as the altitude increases. In the nival zone only few plants, adapted to the unfavourable conditions, can grow. The two altitude record-holders in the Alps are *Ranunculus glacialis* and *Achillea atrata* on the Finsteraarhorn (4270 m). With the present-day climate warming, plants are observed to be encroaching on higher locations. In the highest mountain ranges seed plants grow even above 6000 m, while life in the form of lichens, algae and cyanobacteria reach even higher. In 1972 the Slovene alpinist Aleš Kunaver brought the lichen *Lecanora polytropa* from the south face of Makalu at an altitude of 7400 m. And the fungus *Cercidispora epipolytropa* was growing on this lichen. This is still a world altitude record for lichens and fungi!

Altitude zones can easily be recognized by their characteristic vegetation, but it is quite impossible in this short account to present them for the entire Alps. This is seen in the South-East Limestone Alps, when the Mediterranean oak *Quercus ilex* is not found at the foot of the Julian Alps, but it does occur in the Tagliamento valley in Friuli and then in compact stands more to the west, e.g. in the Adige valley below Rovereto. It

Ranunculus glacialis

Gentiana froelichii subsp. *froelichii*

is completely different in the French Maritime Alps, where *Ceratonia siliqua* and the olive *Olea sativa* occur in the lowest zone. While Mediterranean influences are more or less strong on the southern side of the Alps, they are not found at all on the northern side. The Mediterranean *Cephalaria leucantha*, now known in the Alps only from the strongly Mediterranean-influenced south-western regions, is famous; in the 18th century it still grew in the Upper Soča basin (the Julian Alps) and was described there as *Scabiosa trenta*. On account of the neighbourhood, special floral features occur for example in the south-east of the Alps, where Balkan plants penetrate, e.g. *Drypis spinosa* and *Cardamine glauca*, which are not found at all in other regions of the Alps.

During the Ice Age many plants moved from the north of Europe into the Alps; classic examples are *Dryas octopetala* and *Betula nana*. Quite a number also came from Central Asia, including edelweiss (*Leontopodium alpinum*), which is considered, not quite justifiably, as a symbol of Alpine flora, and predecessors of many species of the *Primula, Pedicularis, Gentiana* and *Saussurea* genera that developed in the Alps.

Knowledge about the life of plants in the Alps also covers, of course, facts relating to their metabolism, their adaptability to the diverse demands of the environment, especially those of the weather, and relating to pollination and dispersal of seeds.

The early researchers of Alpine flora, such as Haller, Villars, Allioni, Wulfen, Hacquet, Hoppe, Sendtner and very many others, at the same time also discovered the world of the Alps. Nowadays, when this "useless world" is no longer unknown or even mysterious, it is mostly subject to harmful human influences and thus in the second half of the 19th century the need for its protection arose, which led to the founding of national parks as protected regions. Such parks in the Alps are, for example, Vanoise, Gran Paradiso, the Swiss National Park, the Hohe Tauern, Berchtesgaden and the Triglav National Park.

The Defereggen mountains [AUSTRIA]

Boris Kryštufek

ALPINE FAUNA

More than two million years ago temperatures dropped drastically. For the first time in the history of the Earth so much ice accumulated at both poles that it did not melt during the short warm periods. The Alps were covered by an uninterrupted blanket of ice, while to the north extended a region of cold steppe, right up to the base of the greatly expanded Scandinavian glacier. The animals retreated southwards to escape the cold. Those species which were able to survive the cold spells along the Mediterranean coast returned towards the north during the warmer interglacial periods, but moved southwards again when the next glacial period occurred. The most important Ice Age refuges were found on the three big peninsulas in southern Europe – the Iberian, the Apennine and the Balkan. In each of these peninsulas geographically separated populations of one and the same species followed their own evolutionary route and gradually developed into recognizable genetic lines or independent species. In spite of this continually evolving process, the glacial periods were essentially an era of extinction. Western Europe entered the era with 47 species of trees and emerged from it with only fifteen.

The constant alternation of glacial shocks with shortish warm interludes shaped the present-day picture of European flora and fauna. When the climate began to warm up approximately 15,000 years ago, foretelling the commencement of the last interglacial period, which we live in today, the glaciers contracted more and more until they remained only on mountain summits and around the North Pole. The species inhabiting the cold steppe and tundra retreated together with the glaciers to regions where living conditions were similar to those before the warming set in. Thus the mountain hare in the Alps remained caught in high-altitude areas, whereas in northern Eurasia it inhabits extensive areas of taiga and tundra. From our standpoint this is a mountain creature, although in the north it is an animal of the lowlands. The altitude in itself has nothing in common with the mountain hare's presence. There are several other shipwreck survivors like this in the Alps: the northern birch mouse, rock ptarmigan, western capercaillie, Ural owl, Eurasian pygmy owl, Eurasian three-toed woodpecker, spotted nutcracker and common redpoll. Many of these species found in Central Europe are not restricted just to the Alps but are encountered in other mountain ranges too (e.g. the Carpathians, the Apennines, the Pyrenees, the Balkan mountains), always being associated with considerable altitudes.

Whereas 10,000 years ago this first group of species followed the cold and the extreme environment, other species penetrated into the Alps, due to the general warming. They came from different directions and survived the peak periods of glacial cold either in one of the Ice Age refuges in southern Europe or somewhere else towards the east, e.g. in the Carpathian basin, in eastern Europe or even in Asia Minor.

In the isolated situation offered by individual refuges they did not manage to develop into independent species, but often recognizable geographical varieties or subspecies came into being. These include the Alpine shrew, blind mole, Alpine salamander and Alpine newt. There is a classic example in three closely related species of rodent: the Alpine, Bavarian and Liechenstein's pine voles. Each of these survived the glacial period in their own Ice Age refuge, where it also finally took shape as a species. Liechenstein's and Alpine pine voles emerged from their refuges to penetrate into the Alps, until they collided in eastern Italy. The Bavarian pine vole, which remained all the time restricted to a small area in the Bavarian Alps, is a rare example of a species that developed in its own refuge on the northern margin of the Alpine glacier.

Only a few species are found today exclusively in the Alps, these being therefore endemic: the Alpine marmot, Alpine ibex and Alpine field mouse. In the mountains of the Balkan and Apennine peninsulas, which unlike the Alps were never icebound in their entirety, the number of endemic species is essentially bigger. The difference is less noticeable among mammals, but more so among reptiles, amphibians and fish, i.e. among cold-blooded vertebrates, which are more sensitive to low temperatures in their environment.

The environment alters in the mountains much more quickly than it does in the lowlands. With every 100 metres increase in altitude, the temperature drops on average by 1°C. Organic nature of course reacts to such a cooling effect. At the foot of the Pohorje range in Slovenia (275 m), the beech is in leaf on average 187 days in the year, at an altitude of 760 metres 163 days, but at 970 metres only 146 days. Just as the vegetative period decreases with increasing altitude, so usually does the number of species as well, because the conditions for their existence become too extreme. With Alpine plants, the number of species is reduced by about 40 for every 100 metres increase in altitude. This decrease in species diversity can differ greatly throughout the entire altitude range. There can be an overall steady decrease, or the number of species can be unchanged up to a particular altitude, and then it drops steeply. Although the number of species at the foot of a mountain is always greater than on its summit, the greatest density of species is often somewhere on the mountain slopes. The reasons for such changes in the altitude distribution are in fact poorly understood but it is indisputable that in mountainous terrain there are more different species than in an equivalent area of level ground. A kilometre in distance is completely different from 1000 metres in altitude – as we all know from personal experience. Mountain regions are therefore very suitable for preserving the variety of the organic world since in a protected area a decidedly greater number of species is included than in an area of equivalent size in a flat or hilly environment. Moreover, human influence is less felt in the mountains. For the visitor, mountains are attractive because of the variety of landscape and the beauty associated with this. So it is not surprising that there are proportionally more protected regions in the mountains, including the Alps, than in the lowland areas of Europe. The first national parks also originated here. Although the main motive for establishing protected regions was to preserve natural beauty rather than biodiversity, the aesthetic aspect had an important side effect in preserving species diversity as well.

In the high mountains, only species capable of appropriate adaptations can brave the extreme environmental conditions. The most obvious advantage is adopting a white colour in winter. The mountain hare can exchange its brown summer coat for white fur in winter and the brown summer plumage of the rock ptarmigan turns to white in snow. On the other hand, the smaller, cold-blooded mountain creatures are usually black (e.g. the Alpine salamander). High-altitude populations of the common viper are similarly black on the whole, whereas those at lower altitudes are brown. Black absorbs heat better, so that dark-coloured animals make more effective use of sunlight, warm up more quickly and in cold weather are less exposed to their hunters.

Winter in the mountains is cold, snowy and long. A protective colour certainly helps animals to escape observation but does not ensure access to food. This can be found under the snow, in the small tunnels which remain under dwarf pine when this is covered by a blanket of snow, or on slopes swept clean by the wind. Many species, especially of birds, leave their high altitudes in winter for lower regions, and they are followed by some mammals. Chamois leave their mountain pastures and head for the forest zone, sunny slopes or river gorges. The Alpine marmot hibernates. During the summer it builds up sufficient stores of subcutaneous fat, which guarantee a source of energy through the long winter for the minimal maintenance of its vital functions. In autumn the marmot blocks up the entrances to its underground burrows, gradually lowers its body temperature (to approximately 5°C), slows down its heart beat and respiration, and remains for a good half of the year in this torpid state. Hibernation is a controlled process. Every so often the animal awakes for a short time, and responds to a drop in the ambient temperature by increasing its consumption of fat. Animals in poor physical condition have reduced chances of surviving the winter since their subcutaneous stores of fat can be used up before the spring warmth comes. Living conditions at high altitudes are brutal and natural selection is merciless.

Unlike the marmot, animals without a constant body temperature (cold-blooded vertebrates) simply become numb in low temperatures. Lacking developed physiological mechanisms for maintaining body temperature, they are completely at the mercy of their environmental conditions. Because of these physiological limitations and their predominantly oviductal method of reproduction, the short summer in the mountains is also a critical period for them. Some species have solved the problem by giving birth to live young. The eggs develop in the mother's body, in two oviducts, which have taken over the function of the uterus. The larvae feed on the egg yolk, and if this is not sufficient, they become cannibalistic.

The female Alpine salamander produces only two young, one from each of the two oviducts. These have eaten their brothers and sisters during their development. While viviparity is the rule among Alpine salamanders, the viviparous lizard and the common viper switch between viviparity and oviductal reproduction, depending on the environment in which they live. In the lowlands, the common viper is generally oviductal, but viviparous in the mountains. Another reproductive particularity is encountered in the Alpine newt. The high-altitude tarns in which this newt lays its eggs are cold for most of the year or even frozen over. Nevertheless the water is a less extreme environment for the newt than the land, so the larvae never completely finish their development but remain in the water for the rest of their life. They do mature sexually but retain their external gills, which are a useful respiratory organ in the water but completely useless on land. This phenomenon, known as neoteny, developed independently in many aquatic environments in the Alps and other mountain ranges (e.g. the Dinaric Alps) as well as in other species of newt, whenever they live in an environment where the land conditions are extreme (e.g. in the Dinaric karst).

In no region have people ever inhabited the mountain world as densely as they have the lowlands. Alpine settlements have always been small and relatively far apart. Human influence on the environment and on animal life has thus been less destructive in the mountains than at low altitudes. In Europe large beasts and birds of prey have been preserved only in the mountain environment of the Carpathians, the Balkan mountains, the Apennines, the Pyrenees and the Alps; everywhere else people have exterminated them. Nevertheless, the Alps have been under greater pressure, so that the wolf and lynx have been exterminated there. Bears have been preserved only in the Adamello Brenta Park in the Italian province of Trento, where their numbers are so low that, viewed long-term, they are doomed to extinction. To prevent this, there is currently a project of resettling Dinaric bears from Slovenia to Adamello Brenta. But the long-term vision sees the future of large beasts of prey in the Alps in their spontaneous spread from the north-west Dinaric Alps and the Apennines. These mountain chains are separated by only small geographical distances. The main obstacle to the return of the wolf, lynx and bear to the Alps is thus not the distances involved but public opinion, which is mostly not favourably inclined to these competitors. From this point of view people find it easier to accept the resettlement of two scavengers, the griffon vulture and the bearded vulture. Many "problematic" species, which were once widespread in Europe, escaped persecution only in the mountains. The golden eagle and the common raven are looked upon as birds of the high mountains, although their presence in the Alps taken purely in itself has nothing to do with high altitudes.

The public often sees hunting as the major problem regarding the preservation of animal species, i.e. outright killing. It is true that in the past unregulated hunting really brought the previously mentioned beasts of prey to the verge of extinction (or pushed them over it), and it also seriously threatened the Alpine ibex and marmot. Yet this is a thing of the past. Nowadays hunting in the Alpine countries is mostly regulated and aimed at a stable equilibrium. But new dangers have appeared and increasingly they are more diversified and more menacing. The Alps have come under great pressure from the tourist industry, mass recreation, the development of traffic and energy infrastructure, global climate change, the introduction of foreign species, etc. If temperatures on the planet continue to rise, the vegetation zones will begin to noticeably move up to ever higher altitudes. Since Alpine tundra in its highest positions will not be able to retreat anywhere else, it will increasingly contract and eventually disappear, and with it the mountain hare and rock ptarmigan as well. Then it will be the turn of the next altitude zone of vegetation and the species dependent on it. This is a foreseeable possible threat of the near future. Some dangers are more easily comprehended and their effects can already be seen but unfortunately we turn a blind eye to them.

In the lake Črno jezero in the Triglav mountain range of Slovenia there used to be an endemic subspecies of the Alpine newt (*Triturus alpestris lacusnigri*). These newts cannot reproduce in an aquatic environment together with fish, and precisely the latter were absent from this glacial lake until man intervened to put them there. A single unconsidered measure thus caused the extinction of this entire local population. There have been many such interventions in the Alps. We will never know about them all, so that we can only guess at what we have already lost in the Alps.

Species:

Alpine field mouse *(Apodemus alpicola)*

Alpine ibex *(Capra ibex)*

Bavarian pine vole *(Microtus bavaricus)*

Rock ptarmigan *(Lagopus mutus)*

Griffon vulture *(Gyps fulvus)*

Northern birch mouse *(Sicista betulina)*

Bearded vulture *(Gypaetus barbatus)*

Liechtenstein's pine vole *(Microtus liechtensteini)*

Western capercaillie *(Tetrao urogallus)*

Common viper *(Vipera berus)*

Chamois *(Rupicapra rupicapra)*

Alpine shrew *(Sorex alpinus)*

Spotted nutcracker *(Nucifraga caryocatactes)*

Common raven *(Corvus corax)*

Eurasian pygmy-owl *(Glaucidium passerinum)*

Common redpoll *(Carduelis flammea)*

Alpine salamander *(Salamandra atra)*

Golden eagle *(Aquila chrysaetos)*

Alpine newt *(Triturus alpinus)*

Mountain hare *(Lepus timidus)*

Lynx *(Lynx lynx)*

Blind mole *(Talpa caeca)*

Alpine marmot *(Marmota marmota)*

Eurasian three-toed woodpecker *(Picoides tridactylus)*

Ural owl *(Strix uralensis)*

Wolf *(Canis lupus)*

Alpine pine vole *(Microtus multiplex)*

Viviparous lizard *(Zootoca vivipara)*

Alpine marmot
(Marmota marmota)

Les Écrins [FRANCE]

Guido Plassmann

ALPINE PROTECTED AREAS

THE LONG ROAD TO CONSERVATION AND SUSTAINABLE DEVELOPMENT IN THE ALPINE REGIONS

OPINION IS DIVIDED AMONG LOCAL RESIDENTS, BUT TOWN DWELLERS ARE APPRECIATIVE: the Alpine protected areas have to tackle many different, contradictory and often emotive issues. The concept of Alpine parks and reserves only dates back to the early 20th century, with the first Alpine national park created just 40 years after the idea first emerged on the international scene with Yellowstone National Park (1872) in the United States. Local residents and visitors often have different views of the protected areas and their usage. Nevertheless, protected areas in the Alps are here to stay, and have been a key economic factor in the development of small Alpine regions for several decades now. Perceptions of the areas are constantly evolving, both in terms of preserving the unique cultural and natural heritage, and of reflecting changing social needs. The Alpine Convention, created in 1991, demands greater cooperation between the Alpine protected areas in order to create a genuine trans-Alpine strategy for nature conservation and sustainable development. National and regional parks, nature and biosphere reserves increasingly form the cornerstone of environmental and economic policy in the Alps, but are also the reason for such policies. The most recent development is the decision to create an Alpine ecological continuum: creating links between territories with strict management coordinated between all types of Alpine protected areas.

THE HISTORY OF ALPINE PROTECTED AREAS

There are many different approaches to protecting natural environments in the Alps, and they have developed over time. It all began in 1914 with the creation of the first Alpine national park in Switzerland, which is still the only national park in the country today. The park was the first self-contained reserve to be established in Europe and the first Alpine national park. The impetus was provided by the Swiss Research Society (Société suisse de recherche) and the Swiss Association for Nature Conservation (Association suisse de protection de la nature). Other pioneering Alpine projects included the

creation of the "Königssee Plant Protection Reserve" (which went on to become the core of Berchtesgaden National Park) in 1910, and La Bérarde park, established in 1913, marking the starting point for France and which later became the central zone of the Écrins National Park. The Gran Paradiso National Park was created in Italy in 1922 and built upon the hunting preserve established in 1856 under Vittorio Emanuele II to protect the last ibex in the Alps, whilst the Stelvio National Park was created in 1935 under Mussolini's regime to protect a vast area owned by South Tyrol and Lombardy. Stelvio is still the largest Italian national park, although it has struggled to gain acceptance and been hampered by complicated legislation which has generated conflicts regarding land use (ski resorts, hunting and agriculture). Most Alpine national parks were created in the 1960s or later: Triglav (Slovenia) 1961 with first Alpine Protection Parc in 1924; La Vanoise (France) 1963; the Écrins (France) 1973; Berchtesgaden (Germany) 1978, and Mercantour (France) 1979. This wave of new arrivals was often marked by conflicts regarding land use, with winter sports causing particular problems. It is hardly surprising that, at the time, some parks were initially seen as a means of offsetting the burgeoning development of tourism, which placed a lot of pressure on the environment.

It took ten years to establish the three sections of the Hohe Tauern National Park (Carinthia in 1981, Salzburg in 1984 and Tyrol in 1991). Unlike their predecessors, the new parks initially combined the notion of a cultural area with a less rigorous conservation focus. Some hunting was permitted, albeit subject to strict rules, and traditional forestry practices continued. In Carinthia, the Nockberge National Park was created in 1987 in the wake of a local protest against the creation of a massive skiing area (in a referendum, 94% of citizens voted against the creation of the huge skiing area). Nevertheless, this national park's protected status was relatively weak and is not accepted by IUCN.

The last wave of national park creations occurred in the 1990s: the Italian Dolomiti Bellunesi and Val Grande in 1990 and 1992 respectively, and the Kalkalpen (1997) and Gesäuse

(2003) in Austria. The most recent national parks in the Alps have gone back to a strong conservation emphasis. The Val Grande National Park contains the first integral nature reserve in the Alps (del Pedum, covering 973 ha), established in 1967. Otherwise, only the Écrins National Park has a similar integral nature reserve (Lauvitel, 700 ha). The status of these integral nature reserves is matched only by the Swiss National Park, with visitors forbidden to leave the marked paths. At the end of the 20th century, after a period during which national parks were less strictly regulated, we saw a return to the original formula: the notion of wilderness referred to in the first Alpine national parks. This can also be seen in the international recognition awarded to the three sections of the Hohe Tauern National Park in September 2006, following the introduction of stricter rules within the protected area.

Particularly since the early 1980s, the Italian Alpine regions have thrown themselves into establishing a multitude of nature and regional parks. These parks have a stronger conservation status than their French counterparts, but management varies from region to region, and from one province (autonomous or otherwise) to the next. Nevertheless the parks are an effective tool for conserving habitats and species; many areas are involved in pioneering work such as the Adamello Brenta, where bears have been reintroduced, and the Giuli Prealpi, which promote high quality local products. By the late 20th century there were around 60 parks in the Italian Alps alone.

Since the late 1990s, a series of nature parks have been created in Austria based on the notion of sustainable development. At the same time, the national parks are striving for a stricter conservation status that will also allow them to be recognised as a national park by the World Conservation Union (IUCN) if the park complies with the criteria for hunting-free areas (e.g. the Hohe Tauern).

There is now a wealth of protected areas in the Alps – 25% of the Alps have an official protection status. Nevertheless, the level of protection varies to reflect the objectives and the cultural and man-made environment (protected landscapes, regional nature parks, biosphere reserves, tranquil zones, nature and national parks, biotopes, nature reserves, integral reserves, etc.). The interpretations and activities on the ground in the different protected areas vary hugely from one country to another and from one Alpine region to the next. Thus the Alps have a highly complementary range of protected areas and their planning (management plans, conservation zones) and use of sophisticated management techniques are increasingly cited as the international benchmark (species monitoring, restoring natural sites, geographical information systems, databases, interpreting satellite images and aerial photographs). The management methods and long-term planning go hand-in-hand with the creation of large areas where the regulations stipulate "no intervention" (as in the case of integral reserves). In the space of one century, land conservation has become much more professional.

SPECIAL STATUS

The UNESCO programme "Man and the Biosphere" formed the basis for the development of biosphere reserves in the Alps from the early 1980s onwards. The reserves combine the conservation of natural resources in a strictly regulated area together with sustainable development measures and the continuation of traditional activities in the remaining area. The reserves are often superimposed on other structures, such as nature parks or reserves, dividing the area into different zones. Monitoring is usually the responsibility of the management body.

UNESCO also classifies natural and cultural monuments as "World Heritage Sites", a label that is highly sought after by many sites, including Alpine protected areas. At present, only three sites have been classified a UNESCO Natural World Heritage Site, all in Switzerland: the Aletsch glacier in the Bernese Oberland, Monte San Giorgio in Ticino and the Sardona Tectonic Arena in eastern Switzerland. A project is currently under way to assess whether to submit a combined application for several Alpine Network areas.

In 1992, the European Union ratified the Habitats Directive, which is designed to protect natural habitats, flora and fauna in Europe. The EU also helped to set up the NATURA 2000 network, which brings together sites representing the continent's ecological diversity. Many Alpine protected areas have been proposed in part or in full and will work to strengthen European legislation on nature conservation.

There is a wide range of other protection statuses internationally. For now, we will just mention the Council of Europe diploma, which, in addition to conferring protected status, constitutes a guarantee of quality for existing protected areas, and the RAMSAR sites, which provide protection for wetlands. The latter tend to be under-represented in the Alps.

FUTURE DEVELOPMENTS AND THE ALPINE CONVENTION

The Alpine protected areas fairly accurately reflect the natural and cultural diversity found in the Alps. However, most of the large protected areas – particularly national parks – are at a high altitude. This raises questions as to their actual contribution as a habitat and refuge for certain highly endangered species that live at lower altitudes. In view of this, one of the Alpine Convention protocols (Protocol on the Conservation of

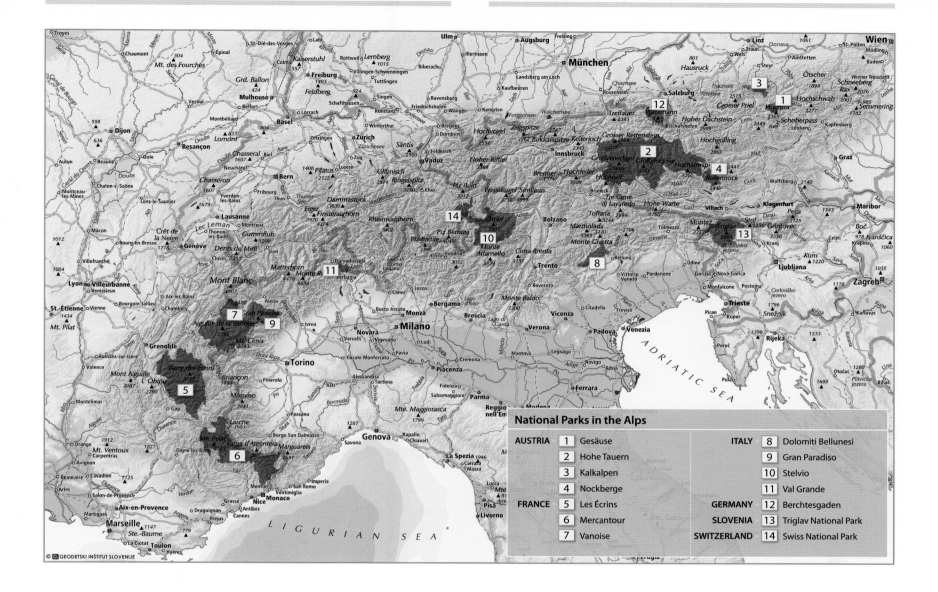

National Parks in the Alps					
AUSTRIA	1	Gesäuse	**ITALY**	8	Dolomiti Bellunesi
	2	Hohe Tauern		9	Gran Paradiso
	3	Kalkalpen		10	Stelvio
	4	Nockberge		11	Val Grande
FRANCE	5	Les Écrins	**GERMANY**	12	Berchtesgaden
	6	Mercantour	**SLOVENIA**	13	Triglav National Park
	7	Vanoise	**SWITZERLAND**	14	Swiss National Park

Nature and the Countryside) provides for the creation of a cross-border network of protected areas: a genuine ecological continuum in the Alps. Working alongside the Alpine Network of Protected Areas, which brings together all protected area managers in the Alps to facilitate discussion and ongoing cooperation, the continuum will establish physical links between the protected areas. Ecological corridors will be one element of the ecological continuum, accompanied by local sustainable land management measures and specific provisions for the various local stakeholders (contractual protection, agro-environmental measures, etc).

Creating strictly regulated protected areas at lower altitudes is another way to link a range of habitats and to compensate for the lack of large protected areas at low altitude. It is vital to link existing natural areas in low level zones (small, well-preserved biotopes, large natural reserves, green belt areas) in order for different species to develop migratory patterns between existing large protected areas in the longer term. In terms of the ecological continuum, this movement could be boosted through zoning and by establishing buffer zones around protected areas in order to reduce the impact of neighbouring towns and villages: protected landscapes and transition zones in biosphere reserves could be used to achieve this. Whatever

happens, we need to adapt the links between protected areas to establish the ecological continuum at a local level, based on an assessment of local potential. Creating Alpine ecological corridors is one of the greatest challenges facing the protected areas and Alpine Convention policy in the coming years.

The protected areas are now a part of regional structure in the Alps: they are spread throughout the Alps, and play a role in conserving endangered species as well as preserving social and cultural life in the Alps, which is being threatened by economic globalisation and land management policies. Certain species that have returned after being eradicated by humans in the early 20th century now use the protected areas as places of sanctuary and in their migrations. The protected areas attract millions of tourists each year and also make an active contribution to the economy and culture in many Alpine regions through their services and activities to educate visitors about the natural and cultural heritage, through their efforts to protect the Alpine landscape and traditional activities, and through their image as places of outstanding beauty.

The Bernese Oberland [SWITZERLAND]

Werner Bätzing

THE LANDSCAPE OF THE ALPS

IS THE TRADITIONAL CULTURAL LANDSCAPE CHANGING INTO A WILDERNESS?

THE TRADITIONAL CULTURAL LANDSCAPE OF THE ALPS

From the time that man had to live as a farmer from agriculture and cattle-rearing, he was forced to alter nature to produce foodstuffs. The first farming societies in the Alps settled here about 6000 BC, when they began to clear the forests to obtain fields and pastures. Thus in the distant past the countryside was greatly altered, with the changes reaching their peak in the Middle Ages, when practically all the more or less suitable surfaces were cultivated. The changes up to the start of the 19th century industrial revolution and up to the beginnings of tourism were no longer so intensive. The medieval appearance of the Alpine cultural landscape was therefore such as was taken for granted in the 19th and 20th centuries. So the Alps have greatly changed ecologically in cultivated areas. These changes can be summarized in four points:

A. Valleys: In valleys and their vicinity (with the exception of flood plains) the forest was completely cleared in order to obtain areas for fields, meadows and settlements. In most cases this land was intensively cultivated, yielding rich crops. The many hedges, terraced fields and small forests contributed to the countryside here within a small area being fashioned attractively and with variety.

B. Slopes: The extensive slopes at medium and higher altitudes were not entirely cleared since the forest had to protect the settlements lower down from dangerous avalanches. Generally the forest in this region was thinned out in the form of a mosaic. Many small meadows and pastures were made in the forest, though fewer on the northern slopes that were snowbound for a longer time than on the southern, sunny slopes, where the forest was more severely thinned out in most cases.

C. Pasture land: The open slopes above the tree-line tend to be small rather than big in the Alps. Because of the millenial-long use of Alpine meadows and pastures for highland farming, the pasture land, firstly, was greatly extended down towards the tree-line, which was consequently lowered by about 300

metres, and, secondly, the composition of the vegetation was essentially altered (more herbaceous plants and less grass, thinning out of bushes such as rhododendron, raspberry, etc). So a cultural landscape must be acknowledged here as well.

D. Flood plains: These are areas in the valley which become flooded every spring. Without human activities, these are places without vegetation (pebbly ground), new grassland and marshy copses (willows, alders).

This region of the Alpine countryside was for a very long time a thorn in the farmer's side in terms of agricultural use, because he could not tame the power of water. Thus for more than a thousand years the flood areas could be used as pasture only when the water level was at its lowest. The flood plains were changed into an intensively worked cultural landscape only in the period 1800-1930; only then were river beds regulated and deepened, flood plains drained, marshy forest reduced and meadows arranged. So it was not the mountainous parts of the Alps that caused people problems for the longest time but the level areas.

E. Uncultivated ground: Alpine areas without vegetation (rocks and glaciers) could not be used agriculturally and thus were not altered ecologically. Such areas held no attraction whatever for farmers; they were regarded as ugly and only an obstacle. So the farmers were really astonished when the first tourists were enthusiastic about these parts of the mountains.

The changes described caused great ecological changes throughout practically all the Alps – only bare surfaces constituted an exception. Since the Alpine landscape is affected by numerous very dynamic processes – avalanches, floods, debris flows and rockslides are constant natural pro-cesses – these changes essentially increase the ecological instability of the Alps. This is a tremendous problem for local people, as their existence in the Alps is directly threatened in this way – the disasters enumerated not only destroy the cultural landscape and thus the very foundations of a farmer's existence, but also directly threaten the life of people in settlements.

Consequently Alpine farming societies especially advocated ways of halting ecological changes in the Alps without increasing their ecological instability. The experiences connected with this are summarized in the following four points.

A. RESTRICTIONS ON USE: Not every mountainside in the Alps can be deforested if we want to avoid risking the dangerous triggering of avalanches. Everywhere specific limits on using Alpine areas must be observed, though these can vary greatly from one valley to another.

B. USE WITHIN A SMALL AREA: The natural landscape of the Alps generally consists of a mosaic of very small areas (moraines on mountain slopes, clearcut borders between damp and dry surfaces), so it is very important that these areas are used within their natural borders and are not altered by linking them together into homogeneous land surfaces.

C. THE RIGHT DEGREE OF USE: In order that the vegetation of a used area can be successfully renewed during and after use, the right degree of use is of decisive importance. Such use must not be either too intensive or too extensive; we must know when to begin and when to finish, i.e. how long the use may last. This is usually precisely defined in the regulations governing land use.

D. CARE AND MAINTENANCE: Despite the recommendations made in the above three points, the cultural landscape is repeatedly endangered, thus additional actions for care and maintenance or repair are essential; these can further stabilize particularly critical parts of the cultural landscape. Primarily this involves regular care (often in spring, when the snow melts) or repairs, which are necessary after a bad storm, for example.

If we pay attention to these four strategies, the cultural landscape of farming areas will be ecologically stable long-term, and can be used for centuries and even millenia without destroying its natural basis. I personally designate this as an active and conscious "reproduction" of the cultural landscape; this has to be "reproduced", because it is not a natural product and cannot be stable simply by itself. Many concrete examples in the Alps show that this reproduction was and is possible. But the first condition for it is that local farming societies act in a responsible way with their own cultural landscape and use much of their working time for this.

REASONS FOR THE DISAPPEARANCE OF THE TRADITIONAL CULTURAL LANDSCAPE

The industrial revolution started a development whereby people exploit the useful parts of nature ever more intensively and the parts that are hard to make use of less and less. For the Alps this means that the *direct use* of their natural resources (agriculture, forestry, mines, extraction industries, hand-manufacture based on natural raw materials) has very much regressed and is centred now only in some suitable areas (mostly in valleys and basins), while *indirect use* has greatly increased: in leisure time and vacations, i.e. the time that has become modern due to industrial development and is based on the beautiful picture of the countryside and the function of the Alps as sports facilities. Analogously, the Alps are considered ideal for the "white" location of postmodern economic plants.

As a result, the Alps have changed enormously in a short space of time. The agricultural use of the Alps, characterized by the decentralized use of cultivated areas, is being greatly reduced and centred only on favourable locations, while at the same time previously quite unknown forms of exploitation are emerging that give the landscape a real urban character.

These new forms are:

A. TOURISM, which increasingly develops in some big tourist centres, which then change into proper towns.

B. LIVING IN THE ALPS, which is attractive for the high quality of life, e.g. in the wider surroundings of swiftly growing Alpine towns or near great cities – a home in the Alps and employment in a big city not too far away (Munich, Milan, Vienna, Zurich).

C. SO-CALLED "UBIQUITOUS" ECONOMIC PLANTS, which have multiplied in the Alps alongside major transit motorways, since these locations are in the very heart of Europe between highly dynamic economic regions and at the same time the Alps give them a high value due to quality living during leisure time. These plants are ubiquitous because they have nothing to do with the specific resources of the Alps themselves (they are more strongly connected with the global or European economy than with the Alps) and could be located anywhere in Europe that linked them with traffic routes.

The common factor in these new forms of exploitation is that they make great use of the Alpine countryside *indirectly* but have no responsibility towards it; this responsibility is given to the state and its experts (regulation of mountain torrents and avalanches).

So it is abundantly clear that because of these changes – reduced direct use of nature and increased indirect use – the Alpine landscape is being completely altered.

ALPINE LANDSCAPES TODAY – A WILDERNESS OR A CULTURAL LANDSCAPE?

Two conflicting directions of development can be established in the Alpine countryside nowadays.

On the one hand, people are moving away from the cultivated regions and the once very widespread farmlands are contracting more and more. Most of these farmlands were formerly forested areas, which means that when farming activities are abandoned, the land is first overgrown with low scrub and then later with forest which is typical of the landscape. At best, this process lasts 80 years, but in unfavourable conditions (high altitude and a dry climate), it can be drawn out for some centuries. Thus the Alps lose their character of an open landscape and become much darker and gloomier. At the moment this process is most evident in the Eastern Alps in Austria, where there are about 100 municipalities with more than 90% forest cover.

On the other hand, suitable areas are being used ever more intensively. These are mostly valleys with the major transit traffic routes through the Alps, which are also very easily accessible via regional roads. Moreover, these valleys and basins are well connected with their nearest big city, while tourist centres beside lakes or high up in mountainous regions are very important too. In all these cases, contemporary intensive exploitation due to the many new buildings (homes, workshops) leads to places quickly changing into towns. Numerous new roads with often unregulated, complicated structures change the remaining available surface areas into islands. On top of everything else there are no end of districts in tourist regions swanking with holiday flats. This means that such regions do not differ in any way from typical "urban landscapes" on the edge of big European cities.

The more this development gallops on, the greater the contrast between mountainsides overgrown with scrub or forest and the lowland part changed into towns – the Alps are changing into two highly contrasting parts.

Both kinds of development involve ecological problems: in lowland towns we are now faced with environmental problems typical of European metropolises – the pollution of land, water and air is admittedly quantatively smaller than in Berlin, Paris or the Ruhr basin but the Alpine relief means that all the pollution becomes very strongly concentrated in particular weather conditions so that the level of air pollution or noise is often the same as in a metropolis. And areas overgrown with scrub or forest go through various transitional phases where they are relatively unstable in ecological terms. In connection with current climate change this leads to increased ecological danger in the Alps due to more frequent avalanches, floods, debris flows and the like.

The biggest environmental problem today is the fundamental attitude towards nature: in the economy just as in personal spending of leisure time, people consider they have the right to exploit nature both indirectly and directly – nature as "material", as the philosopher Martin Heidegger puts it – without having to care about its "reproduction". If for millenia the Alps were a symbol in Europe of dangerous and threatening nature, which man could not control technically – making reproduction within the framework of agricultural use so very important – that experience is changing nowadays, in the postmodern period, and the Alps are becoming a "playground" and "sports facilities", which man can do anything with in order to fulfil his heart's desires. This attitude is to blame for the fact that we can hardly speak any more about responsibility towards the environment.

What should be the way forward? Many people are sad at the loss of the traditional cultural landscape in the Alps, because along with this loss many plant and animal species, most of them rare, are dying out and because many diverse, scattered pictures of the countryside are disappearing, being replaced by monotonous expanses of forest. Some people are enthusiastic about such a development, viewing it as nature being given a free hand again to develop as it likes – the modern expression for such development is "wilderness". Whether there will be a cultural landscape co-shaped by man or a wilderness is thus the central question for the future of the Alps.

The significant point for this question is that a broad discussion about it is needed both within and outside the Alps and that there is no definite answer for the Alps from outside. This was a very widespread problem in the 1970s, when environmentalists outside the Alps quarrelled loudly with farmers and tourist managers in the Alpine region. Consequently it was almost impossible to establish useful connections between the utilization and the protection of nature. Those unproductive conflicts have largely been overcome nowadays, but it is very important that in questions about the future of the Alpine landscape they should not burst into the open again.

Brülisau village [SWITZERLAND]

Bernard Debarbieux

THE ALPINE POPULATION

MYTHS FROM THE PAST
AND CONTEMPORARY CHALLENGES

Professional as well as popular works from the 19th and early 20th centuries, not to mention tourist guide-books, have contributed to a rather simplistic concept of social structure within the Alpine region: these social communities, composed of individuals connected by strong family and religious ties, were assumed in the main not to favour economic and cultural exchanges and to live in close harmony with their surroundings. Europe then created a double myth about the Alpine world: this mountain massif became a model of landscape and nature, while its inhabitants were looked upon as archetypal Europeans, attached to the land, rooted in their locality, adapted to their environment, which they also adapted to themselves.

But in recent decades, some researchers have demonstrated that the reality is quite different. Even before the explosion of tourism, traffic movements in the Alps mingled the population, opened up the local economy and altered artistic and religious sensibilities. The inhabitants of the Alps themselves were among the most mobile, some of them trading and weaving economic and family connections throughout the whole of Europe. And as for the environment, this was far from remaining so firmly established as the myths declared: the little ice age and then the warming which started in the mid 19th century required a series of adaptations from the population; strong demographic growth was unfavourable for forests and pastures; in some places the people had to change their patterns of the economy and their implementation in the natural environment – also under pressure from the state administration. Thus the population of the Alps, as described by historians, differs considerably from that presented by the myth of the Alpine world. And in order to understand contemporary risks and challenges in this region, we ought to continue with research studies and forego idyllic and nostalgic fantasies.

What is Europe like then, what is that world like where the inhabitants of the Alps must find their place nowadays? What sort of challenges await these individuals and groups from now on?

Today Europe and the contemporary world represent a sphere where everything circulates: market goods and energy supplies most definitely, but also individuals, information and cultural patterns. To an ever increasing extent and with ever increasing speed. Sometimes these currents completely by chance go across the Alps and establish contact between the Mediterranean and Atlantic regions, between western and eastern Europe, just as the two base tunnels under the St. Gotthard and Brenner passes, for instance, will re-direct traffic and for better or worse deprive the Alps of this flow. But most currents simply penetrate far into the Alps and more than ever before impact on the everyday lives of the inhabitants. The future of the Alps and of the men and women who live there depends on how they will integrate themselves into these currents, whatever they may be.

Let us consider ideas and values, for western civilizations are individualistic; the development of the individual and his capacity for deciding what kind of lifestyle he will choose, what kind of ties and connections he will opt for, is always important. Even now, and still more so in the coming decades, people will stay, leave or move into the Alps according to their own decision, and that depends a great deal nowadays on the influence of the media and of all forms of communication.

The first challenge is: to what sort of desires and expectations will the Alps give a suitable answer tomorrow? They will not hold onto or invite the type of person that is attracted by big cities – except for some weekend or holiday visit. On the other hand, they may entice those who appreciate nature and the landscape in the Alps and those who find their roots there, whether real or imagined, and create their own social connections.

The decision to settle in the Alps or to move away from them also depends on the economic possibilities. So far the opportunities have been numerous and permanent, especially if we compare them with what could be observed in other mountain regions of Europe, which have remained bereft of population. What will the future bring? In the system of open economies, which predominates today, the accessibility of the places of production is of crucial importance. Many Alpine regions have long enjoyed such accessibility thanks to the railways and especially the motorways crossing the Alps. But what will the situation be like when the base tunnels have taken over the lion's share of transalpine traffic? Except for some points around a tunnel entrance, the Alps will lose some of their relative accessibility. The big cities, where work-places for qualified people continue to increase, will connect these currents, but in relation to the Alps such cities are on the margin, far distant. At best the Alps will attract or retain those who are prepared to make daily journeys between Milan, Munich or Vienna and Alpine villages. Thus the economic future of the Alps lies primarily in the added value created by activities and expertise which are native to this environment, and in private initiative: trades and industries – on condition that the circulation of raw materials and finished products is not hampered; tourist activities – on condition that tourist capital is not lost; the abilities of individuals who know how to create a network of links near and far, which precisely because of new technologies will make possible the development of activities in keeping with state-of-the-art procedures.

But all the same, what will happen to local social groups in a Europe ever more open to the circulation of people, ideas and goods? What binds together the men and women who live in the Alps and those who visit the Alps and travel around them? Asking such a question made no sense in the fine times of the Alpine myth because local communities, obliged to have close interpersonal ties and joint affairs, comprised its basic element. This imaginary world still exists actually, but the reality is much more complex and full of contradictions. There are areas in the Alps, such as southern Piedmont or Provence, where depopulation has reached such a point it is hardly possible to speak of a local community; the economy and the environment feel the consequences of this. There are also tourist regions and valleys in the vicinity of big cities where the number and the diversity of the inhabitants have increased very rapidly, as also in many other places. Is it feasible to speak of local societies in these valleys settled by people who have different goals and habits? One can doubt it at times, if there are few interpersonal contacts and misunderstanding prevails. We know that this happens when newcomers from the cities decide on living in the mountains, but without knowing how to understand and appreciate the lifestyle and work of already established families, such as livestock farmers.

This mixing of the population will mean that in future the Alps will be like the social communities that will form there. These will no longer consist primarily of farmers and stockbreeders but of tradesmen, tourists, commuters, pensioners, salesmen, that is, any and everybody, and they will have to search for what they can have in common. Because probably neither

family origin nor tradition will be significant, because people's interests will increasingly diverge, the inhabitants of the Alps will have to think out what they want to have in common in order to become a social community. Otherwise they will lack initiatives and shared activities. From now on it will definitely be the environment and the quality of life that will constitute this uniting factor, this common goal. In this respect the Alps can pride themselves on having many trump cards: high-quality countryside, diversity of residential environments, density of public services, a variety of economic activities. But none of this is guaranteed long-term. The local residents will be responsible for deciding on what they want to preserve from this heritage and what they want to expand. The actual number of residents, therefore, is less important than their endeavours to realize common goals and their capacities for achieving them, especially where the national heritage is concerned.

Nevertheless it is noticeable that endeavours to realize joint projects and the possibilities for implementing them in the Alps are very unequally distributed. It is almost certain that they will not be found in the most attractive tourist valleys or in the surroundings of towns. Frequently too many economic and therefore conflicting interests occur right there. They are also rarely present in depopulated areas, which have lost many decision-making opportunities. Mostly they will be present in regions which lie somewhere in between, if the circumstances are favourable and perhaps they are blessed with some leading figure or a group of enterprising people. One of the advantages of the increased flow of people and information in Europe is that nowadays such leading persons and groups can establish contacts, exchange information and compare experiences more easily than before. Sometimes organized networks have come into being from such exchanges, and these are increasing all the time: networks of municipalities, tourist centres, protected areas, etc. Although they are often recently formed and the results do not always match expectations, such collaborative networks are certainly one of the forms of operating that need to be taken into account. At the same time they are also some of the lines of force that will shape the Alpine world in the future. Undoubtedly it will be possible with their stimulus to renew local communities in the Alps and a commonality of interests in the entire region of the Alps. In this way a collective identity of the inhabitants can probably be created, a feeling of belonging together, based on related experiences and ideas regarding their common environment and territory. This time a fiction based on an Alpine myth will not suffice.

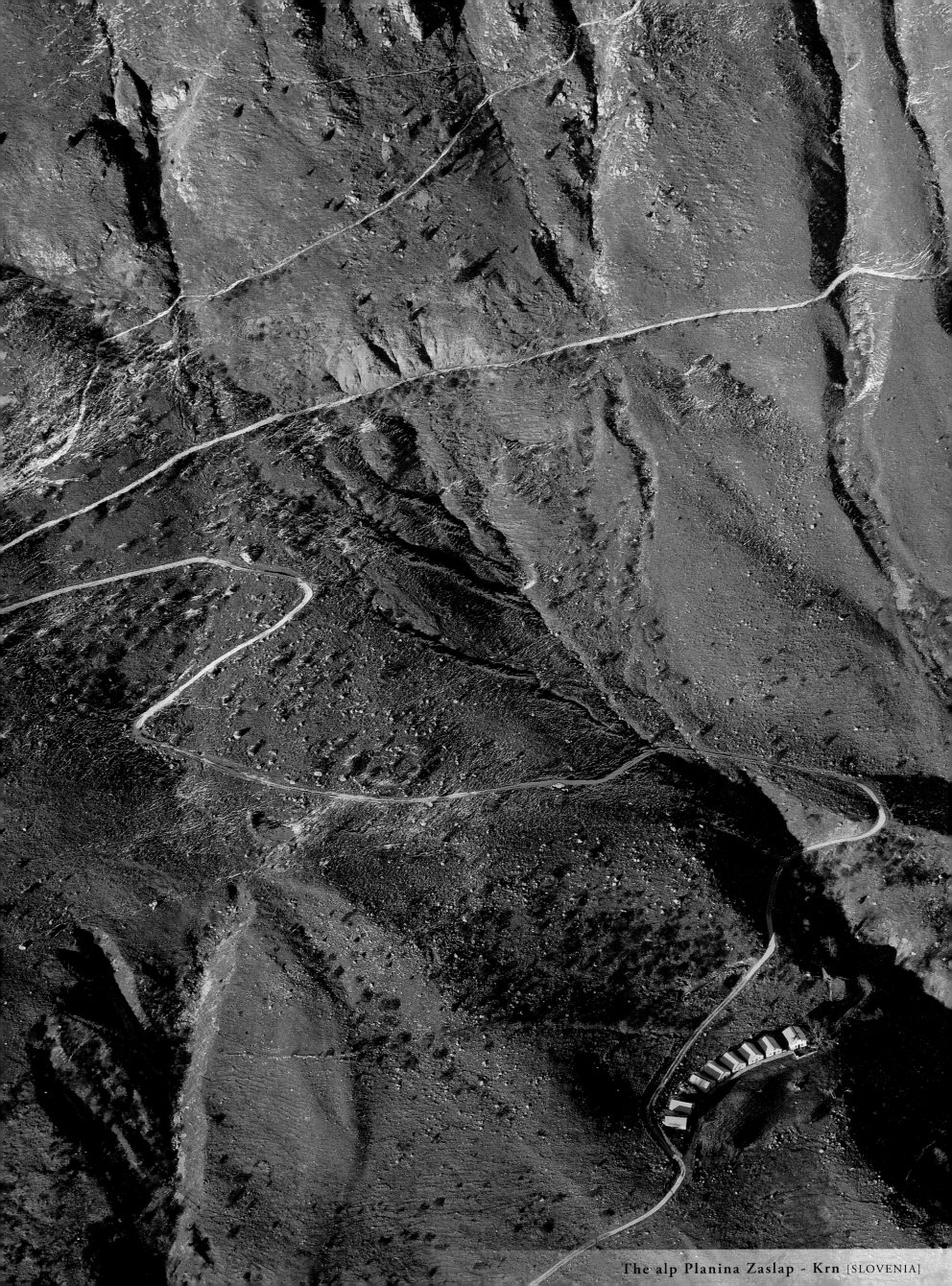

The alp Planina Zaslap - Krn [SLOVENIA]

The Durance River [FRANCE]

Mario F. Broggi

ATTITUDE AND RESPONSIBILITY IN ALPINE TOURISM - WHERE ARE WE GOING?

ILLUSTRATED WITH THREE SWISS EXAMPLES

There is a development in tourism at the moment which we could characterize with the following key notions: increasingly urban or else with an emphasis on smallness, fineness, and nature; shorter but more frequent stays; everything in the interests of health and wellness or else "fun and action". Moreover, overnight accommodation with top-quality infrastructure and a readiness to indulge people seems to suit contemporary tastes. And what is happening to many medium-sized "ordinary" holiday destinations? Do such places come somewhere between these two modern orientations? Or are they entering aggressively upon an "arms race"? Or is there something like a tourist alternative that emphasizes "pure nature"? At present there is quite obviously a flourishing market in North America for environmentally-friendly journeys. They talk there about the "green jet set".
It is well-known that many features from the West have arrived here in Europe as well.
So will the Alps become from the viewpoint of tourism "urban parks" and the rest of the area "wilderness"?
Using three major contemporary Swiss projects as a basis, we will comment on current trends, and hazard a glimpse into the future of the development of Alpine tourism.

ANDERMATT – FROM A "BLACK HOLE" TO "WORLD-CLASS TOURISM"?

Andermatt lies at the northern foot of the famous St Gotthard mountain pass. On a surface area of just under 1.5 million square metres, a top-level tourist destination with several hotels (800 rooms, 600 apartments), 100 holiday cottages, an 18-hole golf course, together with a sports and recreation centre and shops is supposed to be built there. The Egyptian investor Samih Sawiris wants to put a billion dollars into this project. Has Andermatt thus hit the jackpot after this destination was assigned in 2006 to the category of "Alpine uncultivated land", i.e. designated a tourist "no-go area", in one of the highly polemical studies of the Basel branch of the Department of Architecture, Swiss Federal Institute of Technology (ETH) in Zurich?

A visit to the place itself shows that its pervading "Belle Époque" architectural style has acquired some patina and reminds us

that the wonderful times of journeying "across" the Alps have passed. The Swiss army, the biggest local employer, is rapidly with drawing from the St Gotthard massif. So a "black hole" was already programmed. But now it seems a solution has arrived. By "sacrificing the farmers" – this concerns an area occupied by seven farms – it can mostly be realized on the army's land, which has been sold in the meantime (three farmers have left, one has moved to the distant Jura mountains). Discussions are still continuing about further purchases of land. In terms of Swiss conditions, the authorities at the municipality, canton and federal state levels have, with incredible speed, granted permission for everything that has been requested. The Swiss Federal Council has decided that for the sake of the "political interests of the state" it is not necessary to obtain permission to acquire the land, which is otherwise an obligatory requirement for foreigners. The Swiss associations for protecting the environment have been considerably restrained in their criticisms because a Damocles sword hangs over their heads of having a legally established complaint made by an interested association revoked. This revocation was proposed by a political party whose programme is oriented to the economy. What in principle must be said and asked if one stands at more of a distance from the problem? In spite of the great enthusiasm shown in the place itself and the investor's obvious negotiating skills, the following questions and challenges arise:

- *In Switzerland there are basic principles of spatial planning: "long-term sustainable land use", "harmony with the environment", "consideration for the needs of the population and the economy", and "restricting the expansion of populated areas". Can such a huge project be in harmony with these principles? Obviously it can, otherwise the various planning permissions could not be given nor appropriate adaptations be made to the strategic spatial plans. So can all that is planned be squeezed under the cover label of "sustainable" or has this notion simply been overextended?*

- *Was the question of the suitability of the location adequately clarified? After all, this is a so-called "shady hole" in winter and a plateau permanently exposed to wind. So are the two arguments – the amount of land vacated by the army and the weight of the investment – powerful enough? Whoever would want this municipality to have ruined investments in the future!*

- *The core of Andermatt consists of buildings of national importance, thus the appearance of the place and the big projects planned in the immediate vicinity taken together represent an architecturally extremely demanding task. Can undisturbed harmony with the village succeed in terms of both architecture and landscape?*

- *Is this whole project with its great size acceptable for the landscape of a high plateau in the Urseren valley? How can a project marked by superlatives fit in with other structures in the valley, which are predominantly concentrated in a smaller area? The construction of additional infrastructure would be absolutely essential, of course, also on account of the expectations and demands of the target public. And finally, how will the inhabitants of Andermatt identify with the new state of affairs?*

Everything is urgent in this Andermatt progamme, which is understandable from the investor's point of view. But fears that success will be merely short-term are also justified, since a rather artificial world is envisaged and not one that develops from a real place and time. The historical village of Andermatt should be distinguishable from a holiday destination by the Red Sea created overnight, such as the investor obviously was able to present successfully.

"PORTA ALPINA" – A GATEWAY INTO THE ALPINE WORLD - IS THIS GATEWAY ALREADY MAKING POSSIBLE A REGIONAL CREATION OF VALUES?

Almost 57 kilometres long and costing about 70 billion Swiss francs, the Gotthard base tunnel within the European rail network should eventually transport 300 cargo and 100 passenger trains per day.

In 2000, specific groups in the Bünden Surselva region made a public appearance, presenting the idea that the planned emergency station in the middle of the tunnel should be changed into a normal railway station for public use. The

Les Mées

already existing lift for transporting materials in a vertical shaft of the tunnel should be converted into a lift for people when the construction work will be finished. Thus this 800-metre-deep vertical access shaft equipped with a public lift plus a one-kilometre-long horizontal access tunnel would create a connection with the canton of Graubünden. This gateway to Graubünden could be built with additional construction costs amounting to 50 million Swiss francs. In 2006 both politicians and the public in the Bünden region gave their consent for interim investigations. These studies were based on a figure of approximately 200,000 visitors per year, who would arrive roughly every hour at the station in the tunnel, travelling on 16 trains a day. So we must admit that Porta Alpina is a technically fascinating project.

It was even credited with the significance of a survival strategy for the entire mountainous part of the Bünden region. Indeed it illuminated Graubünden like a shining rocket. During the phase of enthusiasm over the project, hardly anyone risked expressing any doubts about it. But after the bright hopes had faded and the smoke had cleared away, and when the cantonal government withdrew from the project in the middle of 2007, the moment arrived for questions, especially in connection with Alpine tourism.

- *This did not employ the traditional model of keeping in step with the old and politically established way of doing things in the region, which prioritizes the doctrine of planning the environment and building infrastructure before new and different developmental strategies are put on the table.*

- *Were they really perfectly serious in thinking that the Portal would enable them to create new values for the surrounding region? Wasn't it simply a matter of fixing up a contradictory individual project lacking any common, harmonized strategy for regional development?*

- *There could have been too few travellers for public transport outside the Portal. Did anyone have any idea at all what positive and negative consequences such a project as Porta Alpina might have for the region? This target-oriented concept threatened to degrade the original potential of nature and culture in the upper Surselva region, which is more clearly present precisely here than in other Alpine valleys.*

Porta Alpina could not have succeeded as an individual project. In this case the Federal Council has taken a great deal of time for its answer – up to 2012. It is quite possible that the technical data for the operation of the tunnel have contributed to the collapse of the project. Its economic aspects also aroused doubts. After all, the basic transport costs per visitor would have been 45.00 Swiss francs. The cantonal government in Bünden "buried" the project in September 2007. But rumours are circulating that the group of private investors have still not abandoned the project.

A COMBINED TOURIST-SPORTS CENTRE AND NATURE PARK IN THE MITTELBÜNDEN REGION?

Savognin lies at an altitude of 1200 metres at the northern foot of the Julier mountain pass on the way to Oberengadin to reach the "top-class destination" of St. Moritz. It was in Savognin that the period of using snow cannon began in Switzerland in 1978, probably because this winter sports centre is situated at a critical altitude. According to predictions regarding current climate change, the snow boundary may have risen by 350 metres by the year 2050. Thus ski regions that lie below 1500 metres will have problems with ensuring snow, and especially there will be no guarantee for ski runs leading into the valley. The inhabitants of the Savognin region have a choice of two options: they can confront climate change by competing with other ski centres and constructing new ski runs and buildings in higher areas where snowfall is more reliable or they can appear on the market more as a tourist destination where the outstanding attractions are: unspoilt nature, variety of culture, and local products with a suitably created new value.

The local authorities obviously wanted to have both options and this is where the problem starts. Together with twenty other municipalities, Savognin is linked into the ambitious Parc Ela project. This 600 km² nature park had its ceremonial opening in June 2006 and now they hope for recognition at the federal level. Around 30 nature park concepts are now competing for the title of a Nature Park of National Significance, for which budgetary funds are also linked with testing the feasibility, equipment and functioning of the park. Individual candidates for recognition as a park must ask themselves where they see a greater value in their specific park and how they differ from the other candidates. Thus, what is their brand, their concept of a park, their unique character built on? Moreover, the Swiss federation has hinted that the municipalities which will be associated in a nature park must include within it the entire area of their municipalities. Yet in the Radons area, in the small municipality of Riom-Parsons, these neighbours of the Savognin municipality, right beside the present boundary of the park, are expected to take over 18 hectares of Alpine meadows at a price of 150 million Swiss francs, and turn this into a building site for a centre (1700 beds), shops, restaurants, and access roads with 1500 parking places. The extended ski areas should also be linked with this. What ought we to say and ask in connection with these two conflicting ideas?

- *The creation of isolated separate zones which, lacking a connection with existing settlements, are consequently rather closed off, contradict the law on spatial planning.*

- *With the Ela nature park, the desire is to offer tourism that is in harmony with nature, especially in summer. But the planned Ra-*

dons project would not contribute to the authenticity which is essential for such a park. In such cases the tourist equipment must be appropriate for the winter months. Without the feature of authenticity the Swiss Federal Council cannot acknowledge the park's application.

- *The responsible officials in the region clearly are still not fully aware of the total orientation to authenticity of a nature park. This is probably true if we hear that further projects are also planned in this region for a hydroelectric power station, which would certainly affect sections of the natural rivers. In Switzerland more than 90% of the potential water power is utilized. Water power is admittedly clean, native to the region and, above all, renewable, but it is not the same as a landscape. In nature parks, special attention must be paid to the undisturbed flow of watercourses. Where else indeed, if not here? The construction of a new hydroelectric power station simply does not belong in a park.*

The speculative Radons project surprisingly went up in flames in November 2007, since voters in the Riom municipality rejected the necessary change of use of the area in the spatial plan. Now the situation again looks better for the regional Ela nature park.

TWO CONFLICTING ORIENTATIONS IN MOUNTAIN REGIONS?

What do these three Swiss studies of examples tell us? The present tourist development in the Alpine region is characterized by two major orientations. By establishing big nature parks, the planners are supposed to stimulate long-term tourist development, especially in economically remote regions. In addition to protecting nature and the landscape, local initiatives are meant to strengthen economic currents in their region. Initiatives of this type have long been known from Italy and France. The Logarska dolina nature park in Slovenia, which is under private leadership, is also an instructive example of this kind. In the "Future of the Alps" programme, this initiative even obtained a CIPRA Alpine award (i.e. from the International Commission for the Protection of the Alps). There too the marketing of regional products is closely linked with the creation of new workplaces and the preservation of the cultural landscape.

But on the other hand the trend towards tourist projects which occupy a large surface area is found in a small number of destinations with a vertical association. Much then depends just on one single firm. But it cannot be denied that this model has its attractive side too. One model advocates the preservation of an unspoilt countryside, the other introduces measures that require the countryside to be organized so that it could adapt to urban forms of life with a ski circus (sun, fun and action). This form has been familiar for some time from the French Alps.

THE CONCENTRATION OF WINTER SPORTS IN SOME TOP-CLASS CENTRES?

Experts are of the opinion that winter sports will probably be concentrated in future in some of the best centres (cf. the market brand "Top of the world"). Then the emigration of winter tourism to these centres will be still more intensive and the trend of connecting with other activities will be easier. Here the idea of tourist-sports centres has its opportunity. Winter sports centres obviously suit a social orientation, rather like city shopping centres. Projects of this kind must be financed by investors or international investment companies. For several decades non-natural urban places have been developing at higher altitudes in the French Alps, the so-called resort towns. In Switzerland such structures are also multiplying in the Unterwallis region (Verbier, Anzère, Haut-Nendaz and Crans-Montana). Foreign investors believe that Parliament will grant them exceptional permission, as in the case of Andermatt. But in these cases too, the basic principles of spatial planning apply. Most certainly there must not be isolated locations on green pastureland or on the haymeadows of the Alpine foothills.

In the projects mentioned by way of introduction, it hits one in the eye that the criterion of availability of land has a special role in the choice of a location. Similarly, subventions from the public sector have also a special role in Alpine tourism. The picture of cost-effectiveness can be highly skewed because of these.

WILL "GREEN" TOURISM BE IN KEEPING WITH THE TRENDS?

It is part of the image of the Alps that tourism has a dominant position here. Yet in the entire mountain chain this is true only for one out of ten municipalities. On the southern side of the Alps the municipalities emptied during the 20th century and in the mid-term this can happen on the northern side as well. Still, the effects of changed structure and global warming offer possibilities as well from one case to another. At present, frequently 90% of all the cable car capacities operate in winter and the once dominant summer tourism has become a sideline activity.

Cannot the Alps – precisely because of global warming – become a destination for wellness and "summer freshness" (in the true meaning of the word) after the temperature in the Mediterranean will have become permanently higher than 40°C? The short summer tourist season could then be extended. South Tyrol with its "four-seasons tourism" has long shown us a fine example of this. Many tourist experts and responsible officials at the regional level have so far only been dismissive about "non-aggressive or ecological tourism" and treated it merely as a less profitable niche. And as a matter of fact, it does represent at present only slightly more than 5% in the whole range of Alpine tourism. But it is possible to extend it. In this connection let us recall parallel discussions concerning energy questions, where for a long time alternative solutions were given very little attention. It is well-known that something carries weight if it is big and so needs a greater investment.

In agriculture there is a well-known saying, "Many small animals also provide manure". So doesn't appropriate tourism, offering responsible journeys to visit natural and cultural landscapes, where the environment is preserved and the local population gains some income, have some potential?

In recent years the slogan "natural life" has become increasingly atttractive. About 30-40% of tourists from the German-speaking countries are especially keen on ecological tourism. The "civilized middle class" is willing to pay a suitable price for environment- and society-friendly tourism. In North America the market for nature-friendly trips is flourishing, and at the moment is growing three times faster than that for ordinary trips. Nowadays every third American adult is supposed to be an "ecology connoisseur" (market estimate in the USA – 77 milliard American dollars annually). Here they lay their bets on a higher lifestyle level, for one generation with social responsibility, but nevertheless this new lifestyle must still offer luxury. The "green jet set" explore nature, have a cuisine based on our grandmothers' recipes, using local products of course, enjoy picnics by the Tennessee River, listen to a story-teller at dusk and relish the good feeling that they have rescued a small item of cultural wealth from extinction (Simone Ott, Oeko-Jetset, *Neue Zürcher Zeitung*, 20 May 2007).

So there is money to be earned with "green" tourism. We are following the initial development of nature parks in Switzerland with great interest. It would be appropriate to link this development with the "slow food" movement, which derives from Italy and already has many adherents throughout the world, also because it rediscovers regional qualities, and advocates short journeys to transport produce and agricultural biodiversity. This attitude to nature and the inclusion of comfort as a new lifestyle are still rather superficial, at least in Switzerland. We will see what the "west wind" will bring in this domain.

CONCLUSION

1. Tourist centres in the Alps will be extended, and will form a possible answer to social mega orientations. But the number of such centres ought to be restricted according to regions, e.g. for Switzerland there could be a bare dozen, and their realization ought to be based on the fulfilment of certain conditions, such as compatibility with the fundamental principles of spatial planning and with tourism itself. If they have a sufficient bed capacity, they will be interesting for tourist agencies.

2. "Green tourism", which constitutes a value, is an economic alternative in the Alpine region that has so far been underestimated. The idea of a nature park in its further development is promising, but authenticity will remain a significant keyword in this case.

3. These two big trends of (a) concentration on winter sports and (b) alternative nature tourism cannot both be followed in one and the same place. Local decisions are essential as to where a particular strategy will develop. "Small is beautiful" can be a middle-of-the-road position for many destinations and can facilitate an orientation towards family tourism.

A "phantom" picture of a "green jet setter":

- aged between 35 and 75 years

- has tertiary education

- has a regular income

- comes from densely populated areas

- wants a holiday offering more in the way of quiet rest than entertainment and activity

- wants to return to what is moderate, reasonable, genuine, and to the value of wellness

- wants to get to know a region and its variety of nature and culture

- wants to have a comfortable vacation, likes good food and drink, and prefers regional products

- prefers the small-scale to internationally well-known destinations

- is also prepared to contribute something for nature conservation.

Above the Matterhorn north face

ABOUT THE PHOTOGRAPHER

MATEVŽ LENARČIČ, B.Sc.

Born: 22. 5. 1959, Trbovlje
Education: graduate biologist
Profession: professional photographer, pilot

ACTIVITY FIELDS:
Biologist: 1986-1990 Institute of the Republic
of Slovenia for Nature Conservation
Professional photographer: www.aerovizija.com
Author of 7 photomonographs:
Around the Only World, 2000
The Upper Savinja Valley, 1991
Waters in Slovenia, 1995
The Savinja River, 1997
The Logar Valley Nature Park, 1996
Šmarna gora, 1998
The Slovene Mediterranean, 1998
51 wall calendars
28 one-man exhibitions
Writer: Author of two books
Around the Only World, 2006
Sense and Realization – Patagonia, 1988

Aviation Expeditions: www.wingsforever.com
World Trans-Siberia, 2002
Around The World, 2004
Africa – Valley of Life, 2005
Climbing Expeditions:
Greenland, 1978
Annapurna I, 1983
Annapurna IV, 1994
Karakorum Himalaya, 1986
Patagonia: Fitz Roy, Cerro Torre, 1983, 1985
Africa, etc.
Paraglider: 15 years' experience, flying from the
mountains of Slovenia to the Himalaya
Pilot: PPL – IFR, 2500+ hours

AERIAL PHOTOGRAPY OF THE ALPS

The Alps are a marvellous chain of mountains, which were formed through the earth's tectonic activity and shaped by the action of climatic factors, yet settlers and visitors have also added their cultural and spiritual dimension. This region of innumerable summits, deep valleys and gorges, lakes and glaciers, settlements and pastures, fauna and flora, rugged wilderness and cultural landscapes can be comprehended as a whole only when we adopt a definite critical attitude towards it, a position where our gaze encompasses everything, yet at the same time picks out the details. Such an experience is possible only from a light plane, which feels every movement of thermal currents, which is slow enough for the pilot to see climbers on a ridge but simultaneously quick enough to cover the 1200 km between Monaco and Vienna in a single flight. The realization that people from different valleys, with different skin colours and different histories, climb mountains in order to experience similar things gives an added value to one's response to a lifeless, stony landscape. An aerial perspective reveals that the Alpine ecosystem has been constructed by people who shaped their surroundings with an awareness of their dependence on nature, but also by other people, who have trodden underfoot millenium-old principles of the region in their greed for profit. From the air one also sees that the Verdon gorges in France, the Mont Blanc glaciers, the granite walls of Bregaglia, the baroque ridges of the Dolomites, and the light-coloured limestone faces of the Julian Alps are natural jewels within the same region, which must be protected at any cost against aggressive exploitation and be preserved for future generations.

THE PIPISTREL SINUS 912 AIRCRAFT

For aerial photography a plane is needed that can rise to the desired altitude and a suitable position for good shots. In mountainous regions the choice is limited due to the great heights, strong winds, weather difficulties, long distances and restricted possibilities for landing. The easiest method is to photograph from a sufficiently powerful helicopter, which can climb high enough, but ecologically

this approach is very questionable, financially extremely expensive and logistically difficult to accomplish within only a three-year period.

The entire photographic part of this project was planned on the basis of one light aircraft used by one pilot, who was at the same time the photographer and organizer. The ecological, ultra-light motorglider Pipistrel Sinus 912 was considered to be very suitable, especially on account of its great speed range (60-220 km/h), economical use of fuel, low emissions and low noise level. In addition, it can reach a height of 6000 m, and fly for over 15 hours without needing to land. These advantages are made possible by its contemporary aerodynamic design and its economical, merely 80 KM engine.

Flying in such a light plane in bad weather conditions is very demanding, as it is so much more sensitive to what is happening in the atmosphere. Flying in a strong thermal is very unpleasant, while photography is much more difficult. Ice quickly forms on the laminated profile of the wings, while the insulation and heating of the cockpit in polar temperatures during winter does not ensure any special comfort. The prescribed instruments are also insufficient for safe flying in purely instrumental conditions. Thus flights in such an aircraft demand a high degree of humility in the face of the natural elements, and a thorough acquaintance with the environment and the weather.
But in favourable conditions such flying means fantastic enjoyment.

THE WEATHER

Because of the very diverse configuration of the Alps, their geographical position between the Mediterranean Sea and continental Europe, and the distribution of air masses, the weather in this region varies immensely and is difficult to predict. Weather factors on a broader scale combine with local phenomena, which additionally complicate the situation in the atmosphere.
Mountain flying is a special and demanding type of piloting. In the mountains the weather changes are quicker and on a bigger scale. Different kinds of rock, valleys and plateaus warm up at different rates, which produces complicated thermal patterns, the moisture from valleys with lakes or from frontal disturbances condenses on cold summits, air masses descend and rise, and their speed is abnormally increased in narrow valleys and notches. Descending air masses on the sheltered side of a ridge quickly outstrip the glider's ability to climb, and despite full throttle being applied, it plunges desperately into the depths. In the mountains there are decidedly

fewer possibilities for making emergency landings due to engine failure or bad weather, and even those rare chances are exacerbated by the complex currents of air masses in narrow valleys.

FLIGHT PREPARATION

It is possible with the Sinus to fly over the entire Alpine chain in a good five hours. But on the way there are so many wonderful peaks, furrowed glaciers, dark gorges, lakes and alps that these 5 hours can easily be stretched to 500, if we want to know them in more detail. Hundreds of summits, ridges, silhouettes melt into infinity. The typical shapes, which we generally know from ground level, are seen in a completely new, unfamiliar light. The mountain tops are lower, the faces different, the ridges join in different places and muddle one's orientation.

For every flight precise preparations are required, which include the geographical study of the region, the choice of locations for photographing, making the flight plan, preparing the aircraft and photographic equipment, studying the weather conditions and the specific lighting details of individual mountains, etc. The flight plan must also take into account all the regulations in the Alpine countries with their differently controlled regions, as well as the daily NOTAM (notice to airmen) restrictions.
Thus the success of any flight depends on numerous factors. Being a one-man crew was a great advantage, since there was no need to harmonize timetables with fellow travellers.
Since the glider makes a minimal intervention in the natural environment, we obtained operating permission from some national parks, even though we needed to take photographs within the park boundaries below the permitted altitude.
The plane was always equipped with VFR (visual flight rules) aviation maps, which made possible safe flying and good communications with control towers. There were also numerous other maps, showing a particular area in more detail, facilitating accurate orientation and recognition of the items to be photographed. Navigation was done with a GPS device, to which the camera was also connected; the latter recorded the exact co-ordinates and altitude for each individual photograph.

Since the highest mountains were photographed from an altitude close to 6000 m, and it was sometimes necessary, due to bad weather, to fly high above a solid layer of cloud covering the topmost summits, additional oxygen equipment was also carried on the plane.

Difficulties caused by the lack of oxygen can occur above 4000 m, on account of a sudden change in altitude.

Obligatory equipment on the plane also included a tent, warm clothing and survival equipment in case of a forced landing on inhospitable terrain.

PHOTOGRAPHY

Aerial photography requires reliable and high-quality equipment. Scenes follow each other extremely quickly, so instantaneous reactions, choice of composition and a great number of shots are necessary. All the photographs for the project The Alps – A Bird's-Eye View were taken with professional, high-resolution Nikon digital cameras from the D2 and D3 series and Nikon lenses of the best quality. Since the window of the aircraft essentially reduces the quality of the picture, photographs were always taken through an open window. Some views were shot in different seasons of the year and in different lighting conditions.

For a good photograph the type of light is of paramount importance. In full daylight all the mountains look very similar. Only special moments, in the early morning or evening with their warm colours and soft transitions into shadows, or the light caused by different weather phenomena give the mountains a special character. So the usual flying day almost always started long before sunrise and ended as darkness was falling.

In one day of flying and photographing about 3000 new pictures were taken on average. This represents an enormous quantity of data, which during the flight was periodically transferred from memory cards in the camera to a hard disk. In the course of three years this amounted to over 100,000 technically flawless photographs.

The selection of photographs was made on the basis of several criteria:
- thematic suitability in terms of the book's message;
- a suitable distribution of photographs from the entire Alpine region;
- a presentation of varied landscape characteristics;
- a presentation of mountains with a special historical, cultural identity;
- a presentation of typical settlements, lakes, rivers, valleys and geomorphological particularities;
- appropriate colour and variety;
- technical suitability for big enlargements.

Sometimes it was very difficult to identify specific but less well-known summits; in such cases the co-ordinates together with the altitude recorded for each picture (exif) were of key importance – data obtained through connecting the camera and GPS device. The co-ordinates, entered in the Google Earth internet program, made possible the accurate determination of the location and direction of taking photographs. Individual summits were then identified with the help of comparable photographs from the literature and the internet. All the data were additionally checked by the expert group for the project The Alps – A Bird's-Eye View.

THE ECOLOGICAL IMPACT OF THE PROJECT

The flight statistics:
- 346 flight hours, 12 of which were spent gliding without the engine;
- approximately 61,000 km flown;
- approximately 3400 litres of unleaded petrol, super 95 grade, as used for cars;
- the maximum altitude reached in flying - 5975 m;
- the minimum altitude reached in flying - 100 m;
- CO_2 emissions: estimated at 7000 kg;
- the noise level: 300 m from the plane 32 dBA (the normal 55% power for the engine during flight).

The amount of fuel used was at least 20 times less than that used by an average helicopter, while the noise and exhaust fumes even just 500 m away from the aircraft are negligible. The Pipistrel Sinus 912 is one of the very few planes to hold the Swiss Ecolight certificate. The aircraft was made in the Pipistrel factory, which with its solar power plant is autonomous and annually saves 180,600 kg of CO_2 emissions. During the entire project the aircraft emitted approximately 7000 kg CO_2 (this amount roughly corresponds to the exhaust fumes emitted by a businessman's car in one year), which can be absorbed by about 300 average, healthy trees in one year. In the three years there was not a single instance of a close encounter with birds, and the plane never descended so low that it would frighten wild animals or visitors. All these factors contributed to the presence of the aircraft having only a small influence on the sensitive Alpine ecosystem.

We are convinced that the positive effect of the project in the form of promoting the development of the Alps in harmony with nature will considerably exceed the direct negative effects caused by the project to the sensitive alpine environment.

AUTHORS OF THE TEXTS

Sir Christian BONINGTON

He was educated at University College School, London and the Royal Military Academy, Sandhurst. Having started climbing when sixteen, he reached a high standard of rock climbing while still in his teens. Invited to join the Joint British-Indian-Nepalese Services Expedition to Annapurna II (7937m) in 1960, he reached the summit. With climbing friends he successfully organized several highly demanding expeditions to the world's loftiest mountain ranges. He has written over 20 books, received honorary doctorates and many awards, becoming an indisputable authority and a legend in world alpinism. His exploits in high mountains are milestones in alpinism, inspiring younger generations. See also **http://www.bonington.com/biog.pdf**

Foto Heinz Bayer, Salzburg

Dr Werner BÄTZING

He studied Lutheran theology and philosophy at Bielefeld, Tübingen and Heidelberg. He then worked as a bookseller in various bookshops and publishing houses in Berlin. In 1983-87 in Berlin he studied geography and philosophy with special emphasis on the Alps. During 1988-95 he was research assistant and then Assistant Professor at the Geographical Institute of the University of Bern, Switzerland. Since 1995 he has been Full Professor of Cultural Geography at the University of Erlangen. He has written numerous works on the Alps. His most important book, *Die Alpen* (1984, 1991 and 2003), was also published in French (Lausanne 2005) and Italian (Turin 2005) versions. His two-part mountaineering guidebook, *Grande Traversata delle Alpi/GTA*, reached its 5th edition in 2006. Publications: **www.geographie.uni-erlangen.de/wbaetz**

Janez BIZJAK, B. Arch.

He is an architect, designer, alpinist (Greenland, Alaska), nature conservationist and publicist. At the University of Ljubljana he studied architecture, visual communication and ethnology, graduating in 1967. After working as a freelance architect (1968-83), he was employed at the Triglav National Park, responsible for the cultural heritage and area planning; in 1992-2005 he was the TNP director. Since 2006 he has been director of the private Alps Institute. In 1985-99 he was a member of CIPRA Slovenia, and in 1992-99 its president. During 1990-94 he represented Slovenia in the Mountain Protection Commission at UIAA, in 1995-2005 represented Slovenia in ALPARC, and in 2000-05 was its vice-president. He has written two independent books and 117 professional articles on nature conservation and protection of the environment, published at home and abroad.

Hervé CORTOT, B. Sc.

He trained as a geographer and glaciologist, then graduated in continental ecology. His passion for active mountaineering in all its forms (climbing, trekking, skiing and cross-country skiing) enabled him to join the Les Écrins National Park in 1977. Starting as a field agent and park ranger, then working as an area manager, he has been Head of the Science Department since 2001. As a scientist-generalist, he is open to human sciences, archaeology and ornithology, as well as to local know-how or landscape management. Curiosity drives him forward!

Dr Boštjan ANKO

He graduated in forestry at the University of Ljubljana. In Canada he graduated at the Ontario College of Education, then taught at high school and directed a Slovene school. He was also a reporter for the Delo newspaper from Canada and Mexico. He gained his M.Sc. at the Yale School of Forestry and Environmental Studies and his Ph.D. in Ljubljana. He has dedicated his attention to landscape ecology, functions of the forest, urban forestry, the history of forestry and nature conservation, carrying out research, publishing and lecturing at the Biotechnical Faculty, University of Ljubljana in these fields. He also developed the postgraduate study "Protection of the natural heritage". He has actively represented Slovenia in research and professional organizations and forums, lectured at scientific meetings and as guest lecturer at many universities. The core of his work remains man's attitude to the forest and to nature in general.

Dr Anton BRANCELJ

He obtained his Ph.D. in 1991 with the thesis "A model of zooplankton production assessed in *Daphnia hyalina* (Crustacea: Cladocera) in the lake Blejsko jezero". Since 1983 he has been employed as a full-time researcher at the National Institute of Biology in Ljubljana, becoming an Associate Professor, and has been a department head since 1994. He began research into high-mountain lakes in the Julian Alps in 1991. Since then he has participated in three international projects on high-mountain lakes in Europe and conducted two national projects on the same topic. He and his co-workers presented the results of this research in High-mountain Lakes in the Western Part of the Julian Alps (2002) and in other scientific papers.

Dr Mario F. BROGGI

He studied forestry at the ETH, Zurich and gained his Ph.D. at the University of Bodenkultur in Vienna. He was lecturer at the Universities of Basel and Vienna. For 29 years he worked as an independent ecologist at offices in Liechtenstein, Zurich, Vorarlberg and Vienna. In 1998-2004 he was Director of the Institute for Forest, Snow and landscape (WSL) at ETH. He cooperates in various international organizations: the Council of Europe, IUCN, IUFRO and CIPRA, where for several years he was president. At present he is university adviser at Liechtenstein University and co-worker in many nature conservation foundations. He has written over 300 professional publications on ecology, agriculture, forestry and area planning.

Dr Lučka KAJFEŽ BOGATAJ

In 1980 she graduated at the Faculty of Mathematics and Physics and gained her Ph.D. at the Biotehnical Faculty, University of Ljubljana. Since 1997 she has been Full Professor, lecturing at both faculties. Since 1996 she has been head of the Biometeorology Centre at the Biotehnical Faculty. During 2002-08 she was a member of the Intergovernmental Panel for Climate Change (IPCC) in Geneva and since 2006 has been a committee member of the Global Climate Observation System (GCOS) at the WMO. Her research deals with climate change and applicative meteorology. She has published 87 research articles, more than 400 professional and popular-scientific articles and in 2008 the book *Kaj nam prinašajo podnebne spremembe? (What does Climate Change Bring Us?)*. She received the City of Ljubljana Award 2008, the Order of Merit of the Republic of Slovenia, the Roža Mogota award 2008, and as an IPCC member shared in the Nobel Peace Prize 2007.

Dr Bernard DEBARBIEUX

Since 2001 he has been Professor of Cultural and Political Geography at the University of Geneva; he is also an expert on social and political issues concerning mountain regions and related activities. His research deals primarily with geography, tourism and the landscape. His main field of interest is the mountains of Europe and North America. Within the framework of DATAR (Délégation à l'Aménagement du Territoire et à l'Action Régionale) (Paris) he headed a research group for the project "Representations and Territorial Complexity". At present he is head of a research group dealing with "Mountains: Knowledge and Politics".
For more information see **http://www.unige.ch/ses/geo/ collaborateurs/enseignants/debarbieuxbernard.html**

Dr Hans HAID

He gained his Ph.D. in european ethnology at Vienna University. The author of numerous books on the Alps and participant in many well-received radio programmes, he has worked since 1972 as freelance writer, lecturer, researcher into the Alpine cultural tradition and organizer of many international meetings. In 1974 he won the Peter Rosegger Prize, Staackmann publishing house. He co-founded the International Dialect Institute and founded the association Pro Vita Alpina/International. The Binding Foundation of Liechtenstein, awarded him the Great Binding Prize in 1997 for conservation of nature and environment, Bavarian Television the Grüner Oscar award in 1999, and in 2007 the Austrian President Heinz Fischer awarded him the honorary title of Professor.

Dr Boris KRYŠTUFEK

As Professor of Zoology, he is Head of the Institute for Biodiversity Studies at the Science and Research Centre of Koper, the University of Primorska, and Head of the Vertebrate Department at the Natural History Museum of Slovenia. He studies mammals of the Balkan peninsula, and of the Near and Middle East. Independently or with his colleagues he has published or edited several books: Sesalci Slovenije (*Mammals of Slovenia*), Sesalci Turčije in Cipra (*Mammals of Turkey and Cyprus*), Atlas sesalcev Evrope (*Atlas of European Mammals*), Biodiverziteta Balkana (*The Biodiversity of the Balkans*), Živeti z medvedi (*Living with Bears*), etc. He is a subject editor of the periodical Mammalia, a member of editorial boards of Slovene and international scientific periodicals and heads a variety of national and international research projects.

Marco ONIDA, LLM

He studied economics and law at the L. Bocconi University, Milan, and gained his LLM in International and Comparative Law at Vrije Universiteit, Brussels. Since 1994 he has been an official of the European Commission, Directorate General for the Environment, and is currently seconded to the Alpine Convention. His present position is Secretary-General of the Alpine Convention (Innsbruck-Bozen) and he is also responsible for the Permanent Secretariat of the Alpine Convention. He is the author of various publications in the field of European and international environmental law.

Dr Michael ZEMP

He graduated in science and gained his Ph.D. at the University of Zurich. Besides his studies he worked as assistant scientist in Natural Catastrophe Risk Management at Winterthur Insurance and later as GIS specialist at ESRI Switzerland. Since 2003 he has been a research associate of the World Glacier Monitoring Service, being engaged in various scientific projects, including scientific working stays with the Fortalecimiento de la Red Ambiental in Colombia, and at the National Snow and Ice Data Center in Boulder, USA. He is a lead author of several publications in scientific journals and peer reviewed books. Most recently, he was responsible for producing a report on "Global Glacier Changes: Facts and Figures".
http://www.grid.unep.ch/glaciers/

Dr Roland DELLAGIACOMA

With a Ph.D. in forestry, at present he is Director of the Office for Nature and Countryside in the provincial government of South Tyrol in Bozen. He is also head of the ARGE-ALP project and a member of various expert committees for area and landscape planning and administering protected nature regions. His main spheres of work are nature conservation, nature parks, rural development, landscape planning and building culture. He has written many professional articles and lectures dealing with nature and the countryside.

Dr Uroš HERLEC

His M.Sc. and Ph.D. study was in the field of geochemical research into the use of stable oxygen and carbon isotopes in ecological and paleoecological studies. In 1995 he undertook further study at the University of Tasmania, Hobart, with an Australian government scholarship. At present he works in the Department of Geology, Faculty of Natural Science and Engineering, University of Ljubljana, lecturing on "Deposits of raw minerals, coal and oil" and "Microscopy of ores and coal". He also actively engages in field research for ore deposits. In 1996-2001 he was president of the Slovene Geological Society and for three years vice-president of the European Federation of Geologists. He has published over 200 research, professional and popular-scientific articles.

Ferdinand LAINER, B. Sc.

In 1984 he graduated in forestry from the University of Natural Resources and Applied Life Sciences, Vienna and took the state examination for senior forestry workers in 1988. During 1985-87 he worked in the Styrian Chamber of Agriculture and Forestry as head of the department for the Upper Mur Valley (Oberes Murtal). Since 1987 he has been employed in the Salzburg administration of the Hohe Tauern National Park, where he is vice-director and responsible for wildlife management, cultural landscape and rural development. His important wildlife projects include: head of the project reintroduction of the Bearded Vulture in the Hohe Tauern, management of game and hunting, telemetric research on the ibex. He manages the European Diploma Area Krimml Falls. During 1995-2007 he headed the LEADER- programme "The Hohe Tauern National Park Region".

Dr Guido PLASSMANN

He studied Alpine geography and history, graduating in 1993. In 1998 he gained his Ph.D. at the Joseph Fourier University of Grenoble. Since 1993 he has worked within the framework of the Alpine Convention and since 1995 has been responsible for developing the network of Alpine protected areas in the Les Écrins National Park and for the French Ministry of the Environment. He is director of the government organisation Alpine Network. Since January 2006 he has been involved in creating the Task Force "Protected Areas of the Alps". Since June 2006 he has been director of the Task Force ALPARC and a member of the Permanent Secretariat of the Alpine Convention. He has written works relevant to protected areas, and is a coordinator of research events (1993 – 2007).

Dr Tone WRABER

He graduated in biology at the University of Ljubljana in 1961 and specialized at the International Station for Alpine and Mediterranean Geobotany in Montpellier. He gained his Ph.D. at the University of Trieste in 1972. In 1960-68 he was curator for botany at the Natural History Museum of Slovenia and in 1968-2003 (until retirement) Full Professor of Systematic Botany and Phytocenology at Ljubljana University. His work has centred on the flora of Slovenia, the western Balkans and the Slovene Alps, the protection of plant life, and the popularization of botany. The editor of *Proteus* and other periodicals, he has also written or co-authored 9 reference books and 2 translations of books on Alpine flora. He participated as botanist in 3 expeditions to the Himalaya and Central Africa.

ACKNOWLEDGEMENTS

The Alps – A Bird's-Eye View is an extensive and complex project,
carried out with the cooperation of many experts, whose contributions have rounded out
the mosaic presentation of this magnificent mountain range. In addition to these,
numerous individuals have supported the project in a variety of ways. This help has been indispensable.
We express our heartfelt thanks to all for their cooperation, for we are well aware
that their real contribution far exceeds the financial capacities of the project.

Gregoire Bel, Jana Bergant, Bogdan Biščak, Dr Mario F. Broggi, Freddy Fortunato, Tine Guzej, Marjutka Hafner, Gerald Imfeld,
Hortensia Eraj, Miha Kovač, Jože Lenič, Anja Leskovar, Dr Andrej Lukšič, Nathalie Morelle, Thomas Oberhauser,
Dr Guido Plassmann, Andreja Peček, Franci Savenc, Alenka Skok, Igor Stanonik, Jernej Stritih, Marjeta Keršič Svetel,
Dr Janez Šumrada, Hugues Thiebault, Davorin Tonkli, Federico Vallauri, Dr Michael Vogel, Matjaž Vrečar, Philippe and Cecile Zen.

INTRODUCTORY PHOTOGRAPHS:

The River Unec at
Planinsko polje (Slovenia)

The Dolomiti Bellunesi
National Park (Italy)

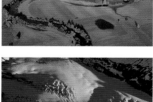

The Grenz Glacier beneath
the north face of Lyskamm
(Switzerland)

The lake Eibsee
(Germany)

The north-west face
of Mont Blanc (France)

KEY TO DOUBLE-PAGE PHOTOGRAPHS:

Pic de Bure, 2709 m [FRANCE]	**N** 44° 36' 13" **E** 05° 54' 23"	⟳ 2714 m
Name, altitude and country	Location when photographing	Altitude when photographing

CONTENTS

THE ALPS
A Bird's-Eye View

Publisher:	PanAlp d.o.o., Savinjska c. 4, 3331 Nazarje, Slovenia
	E-mail: info@panalp.net, www.panalp.net
	© PanAlp d.o.o 2009, All rights reserved
Editorial board:	Vojko Strahovnik / *Editor in Chief*
	Marko Lenarčič / *Member*
	Matevž Lenarčič / *Member*
Expert Council:	Janez Bizjak (SLO)
	Dr Mario Broggi (CH)
	Dr Hans Haid (A)
	Matevž Lenarčič (SLO)
	Dr Guido Plassmann (F)
	Dr Michael Vogel (D)
Photographer, description of the photographs:	Matevž Lenarčič
Text:	Janez Bizjak
Introduction:	Koïchiro Matsuura (J)
	Sir Christian Bonington (GB)
	Marco Onida (I)
Authors of the texts:	Dr Boštjan Anko (SLO)
	Dr Werner Bätzing (D)
	Dr Lučka Kajfež Bogataj (SLO)
	Dr Anton Brancelj (SLO)
	Dr Mario F. Broggi (FL)
	Hervé Cortot (F)
	Dr Bernard Debarbieux (CH)
	Dr Roland Dellagiacoma (I)
	Dr Hans Haid (A)
	Dr Uroš Herlec (SLO)
	Dr Boris Kryštufek (SLO)
	Ferdinand Lainer, DI (A)
	Dr Guido Plassmann (F)
	Dr Tone Wraber (SLO)
	Dr Michael Zemp (CH)
Design:	Ivana Kadivec
Illustrations:	Jaka Modic
Translation:	Dr Margaret Davis
Survey of geographical names:	Dr Stanko Klinar
Maps:	© Geodetski inštitut Slovenije
	Cartographic design and editing: Primož Kete
	Realization: Jani Demšar
Printing:	Korotan, 2009
	1st printrun 5000

www.panalp.net
Design: Ivana Kadivec
Realization: Andreja Vrečar

....
CIP - Kataložni zapis o publikaciji
Narodna in univerzitetna knjižnica, Ljubljana

908(234.3)(084.12)
77.047(234.3)

BIZJAK, Janez, 1943-
   The Alps : A Bird's-Eye View / [text Janez Bizjak] ; photos
Matevž Lenarčič ; [introduction Sir Christian Bonington, Koïchiro Matsuura,
Marco Onida ; illustrations Jaka Modic ; translation Dr Margaret
Davis ; maps Geodetski inštitut Slovenije]. - Nazarje : PanAlp,
2009

ISBN 978-961-6111-19-5
1. Lenarčič, Matevž
244089600

DELO
Gorenjski **Glas**

POP / ▲
24ur.com · poptv.si

I FEEL
SLOVENIA
www.slovenia.info